HEATHER CARMICHAEL'S DIARY ENTRY

I keep telling myself that this nanny job is just temporary, but there's something about the Sheffield house that compels me to stay. I can't quite explain it, but I feel such warmth when I walk up to the fourth floor. It's the oddest sensation—not scary at all. And I know this may sound crazy, but I feel less lonely when I'm there. Almost like someone's beckoning me to stay and fight. . . but for what? My position here?

I was a goner the instant I held baby Yvette and gazed down at those sparkling blue eyes and angelic smile. But I know I can't get attached to Yvette. . . or Maxwell. Especially not Maxwell. It's impossible to ignore that disapproving look on his mother's face whenever we're in the same room together. But what if I told you he kissed me last night? I mean really kissed me. . . ?

Please address questions and book requests to: Silhouette Reader Service
U.S.: 3010 Walden Ave., P.O. Box 1325, Buffalo, NY 14269
Canadian: P.O. Box 609, Fort Erie, Ont. L2A 5X3

MASSACHUSETTS

PHYLLIS HALLDORSON

Only the Nanny Knows for Sure

Silhouette Books

Published by Silhouette Books
America's Publisher of Contemporary Romance

SILHOUETTE BOOKS
300 East 42nd St.,
New York, N.Y. 10017

ISBN 0-373-47171-8

ONLY THE NANNY KNOWS FOR SURE

Copyright © 1990 by Phyllis Halldorson

This edition published by arrangement with Harlequin Books S.A.

® and TM are trademarks of Harlequin Books S.A., used under license.
Trademarks indicated with ® are registered in the United States Patent and
Trademark Office, the Canadian Trade Marks Office and in other countries.

Printed in U.S.A.

Dear Reader,

Several years ago my husband and I attended a writer's conference in Boston, Massachusetts. I was totally captivated by the grand old city that played such a large part in our emerging nation's struggle to be free and vowed to set my next novel against the historical background of Faneuil Hall, which had served as a meeting hall for many stirring meetings during the Revolutionary movement; the Old North Church, where the lantern was hung to alert Paul Revere that the Redcoats were coming; the Old State House, from whose balcony the Declaration of Independence was first read to the people; and the grassy green Lexington Common, on which the first shots of the Revolutionary War were fired.

What better place to tell the story of a blossoming young love and a playful old ghost?

Phyllis Halldorson

Chapter One

Heather Carmichael stepped out of the plane at Boston's Logan International Airport with a tug of apprehension. In her long-distance telephone conversation with Mrs. Beaufort yesterday the other woman had assured Heather that she'd be met at the airport and driven to the offices of the Sheffield law firm for her interview.

The problem was how would the person meeting her recognize her in the big, busy terminal? It's true they had a description of her, but how did you tell one medium-sized young woman with blue eyes and black hair from the dozens of others who would no doubt be milling around?

She'd told Mrs. Beaufort that she'd be wearing a gray suit with an eye-catching red blouse, but when she couldn't find the suit this morning and belatedly remembered that she'd taken it to the cleaners, she had to wear the only other suitable ensemble she owned. A full black skirt and a silky long-sleeved white blouse that tied at the throat with a wide, floppy bow. It looked like a schoolgirl outfit, which is what it was. After three years in college most of her meager wardrobe consisted of worn jeans and shirts.

As she walked up the ramp and into the boarding area, she slowed to look around, and a wave of cold panic swept over her. The flight from Atlanta to Boston had been her first airplane ride ever, and the people at the college had handled all the details of arranging for her ticket and boarding pass and putting her on the right plane.

Now she was all alone in a strange city, with a sea of people streaming past in both directions. Nobody paid any attention to her, and she didn't even know where to go to get her luggage.

Timidly she walked out into the aisle, and it was then that she saw the sign. Held above the heads of the throng was her name, HEATHER CARMICHAEL, printed in bold black print on white cardboard.

With a loud sigh of relief she hurried forward and found a tall, muscular man dressed in a gray uniform holding it. "I'm Heather Carmichael," she said. "Did Mrs. Beaufort send you to meet me?"

They'd sent a chauffeur! He was a big man, probably in his late thirties, with a nose that was a trifle off center as though it had been broken, and a jagged scar on his chin. He put down the sign and looked her over thoroughly with his slitted brown-eyed gaze before answering. "Yeah, I'm Nick. Do you have some identification?"

"What? Oh, yes, yes, of course." She rummaged in her purse and found her driver's license. "Here," she said, and handed it to him. "I also have the confirmation letter from Mrs. Beaufort." She brought out a long envelope and gave it to him, too.

He studied both, then handed them back to her. "Okay, let's go. You do have luggage, don't you?"

She assured him she did, and then almost had to run to keep up with his long-legged stride.

Half an hour later he carried her case outside and set it on the curb. "Wait here," he said briskly. "I'll get the car and bring it around."

Before she could offer to go with him, he took off and left her alone again. Her apprehension returned. "What was she getting herself into? She'd never been this far away from her hometown of Macon, Georgia, before. Of course, she'd spent the past year going to school in Atlanta, but it was a small private college and she'd lived on the grounds, where she felt sheltered and protected. Here she was on her own for the first time in her life.

A long, sleek white limousine drove up beside her, and she looked at it admiringly. The windows were darkened so she couldn't see in, but it was big enough to live in.

She looked around to see if Nick was coming when the door on the driver's side of the limo opened and he stepped out. Good heavens, this was her transportation!

She stood watching in openmouthed amazement while he walked around and stowed her suitcase in the back, then held the door open for her. "You...you mean you want me to ride back here?" she asked stupidly.

He shot her a puzzled look. "That's the idea, unless you'd rather sit up front with me."

She hurriedly retreated backward. All that room and luxury in an automobile was too intimidating for her. "I'd prefer that, if you don't mind."

With an impatient shrug he closed the door and opened the front one for her.

They drove out of the airport and into a narrow tunnel, where they were caught in a traffic snarl that brought them to a halt. "Why are we in a tunnel?" she asked.

Again he looked at her. "Because the airport is on a peninsula across the inner harbor from the main part of the city, and this is the quickest way to come and go."

"Oh," she said, and decided to just keep quiet and stop showing her ignorance.

As they inched along the dimly lit and seemingly endless tube, it was Nick who finally broke the silence. "So you're the Beauforts' nanny," he said. It sounded more like a question than a statement.

"Yes. Well, that is, I hope so. I still have to get through the personal interview." She was beginning to dread that. It would be a disaster if she were too intimidated by the wealth and prestige of the famous Sheffield family to talk coherently.

"You don't look old enough to be a nanny," he observed.

"I'm twenty-one," she said defensively, "and I have a certificate from the Peachtree Nanny College in Atlanta."

Nick chuckled. "Nanny college? What in hell do they teach in a nanny college?"

He was making fun of her, and her hackles rose. "They teach how to be a nanny, which is a lot more involved than just baby-sitting."

He raised one eyebrow. "Oh, how so?"

She opened her mouth, then closed it. *Take it easy, Heather. Don't let him bait you. Show him that you're a Southern lady who is always gracious.*

"A nanny is employed to help raise a child, not to just look after it for a few hours at a time. I'll have full-time care of the baby since both of her parents have careers, and I'll be responsible for teaching her a lot of the things her mother would if she were with her all day."

He didn't look impressed. "I thought women were born knowing how to do that."

"Were you born knowing how to be a father?" she snapped.

He favored her with a wicked grin. "I was born knowing how to *become* a father, if that's what you're asking."

Heather felt the accursed blush that heated her whole body every time she was embarrassed, and she knew she'd stammer if she tried to answer.

Nick must have seen her crimson face because he smiled and patted the hands she was clasping in her lap. "I'm sorry," he said gruffly. "I shouldn't tease you, but you're so cute and innocent that I couldn't resist. Tell me what else you were taught in nanny college. I won't embarrass you again."

She noticed that they'd finally gotten through the underwater passage and were threading their way through the narrow, crowded streets of historic downtown Boston. It would be better to talk than to suffer an uneasy prolonged silence.

"We...we studied child development, infant and child care, nutrition, first aid, life-saving techniques, plus courses in manners and how to conduct ourselves in the society of our wealthy employers."

This time Nick stared at her, and the friendly smile was gone. "I'll be damned," he said angrily. "You really had me going there for a minute. I was willing to believe that you'd gotten into this because you liked kids, but that's not the reason at all. It's the kids' rich parents you're attracted to. It's a backdoor way to bask in the reflected limelight of celebrities and social bigwigs."

Now it was Heather who stared. Who was this... this person...to question her motives? Her embarrassment vanished, and her temper took its place. "Well, look who's talking," she said icily, abandoning her attempt to convince him that she was a Southern lady. "Need I remind you that you're a chauffeur for the same employer?"

He looked momentarily nonplussed, but managed a quick comeback. "Average-wage earners can't afford chauffeurs." His tone was gruff.

"Neither can they afford nannies," she snapped. "You have to be wealthy to hire twenty-four-hour-a-day care for your child, but even so, my wages don't compare with those of a factory worker, and a plumber makes more than both you and me put together."

He didn't answer, and she turned away and looked out her side window until he pulled up in front of a

high-rise building that looked incongruous surrounded by historic two- and three-story structures.

Nick got out of the car and came around to open
the door for her. "The offices of the Sheffield law
firm are on the tenth floor," he told her as she stepped
out onto the sidewalk. "I'll pick you up when you're
finished, so just leave your suitcase with me."

"Thank you," she said abruptly, and turned to
walk, head high and gait graceful, into the lobby, hoping all the while that she wouldn't stumble in her
three-inch heels and fall flat on her face.

Heather got off the elevator on the tenth floor and
found the door to the Sheffield suite. She gave her
name to the pretty young receptionist and was told to
take a seat. A few minutes later the receptionist called
her and led her to a door marked with the discreetly
lettered name, JOCELYN SHEFFIELD, and opened it.

Heather hesitated. "I'm supposed to see Mrs.
Beaufort," she said.

The other woman nodded. "Jocelyn Sheffield *is*
Mrs. Beaufort. She uses her maiden name professionally." She motioned to a chair in front of the desk.
"If you'll sit down, I'll tell Mr. Sheffield that you're
here. He'll be with you in a moment."

Before Heather could protest that her appointment
was with Mrs. Beaufort, not Mr. Sheffield, the receptionist had disappeared and shut the door.

Heather looked around at the elegant office furnished with mahogany and leather. There were original oil paintings on the walls, and exotic plants stra-
tegically placed to make it look more informal, but it
had the aura of power and influence and old money.
It even smelled expensive.

For the second time since getting off the plane, Heather had misgivings about accepting this placement. Until a month ago she'd never have believed that she'd ever be lucky enough to be employed by one of the famous, or in some cases infamous, Sheffield family members.

The prospect was mind-boggling. The Sheffields didn't have a U.S. president in their lineage like the Kennedys, but they traced their ancestors back to the *Mayflower*, and there were enough governors, state and federal senators and colorful lawyers to make them one of the richest, most powerful dynasties in the country. When the school had asked permission to submit her résumé to them for consideration it had been so unreal that she hadn't taken it seriously until she was asked to appear in Boston for a personal interview.

Now she was trapped. She'd accepted their plane ticket for the flight to Boston, and had agreed in writing to take the position of nanny should it be offered. It wasn't excitement that made her heart pound and her stomach lurch, it was fear.

She didn't belong in this environment, and if she had any sense at all she'd run, not walk, to the nearest exit and forget the whole thing.

She clutched the arm of the chair, and had just started to rise when the door opened and the most compelling-looking man she'd ever seen walked in. It wasn't so much his features as the way he carried himself and the air of command about him that magnetized her.

She recognized him as one of the Sheffield brothers, and if she were to describe him he'd sound rather

ordinary. Medium height and weight, brown hair and
green eyes, but there was nothing ordinary about this
man. He was born for greatness, and nothing could
hold him back.

Her legs buckled, and she dropped back down on
the seat, unable to tear her gaze away from him as he
nodded and walked toward her to sit in the upholstered executive chair on the other side of the desk.

"Good afternoon," he said as he opened the folder
he carried. "I'm Maxwell Sheffield, Mrs. Beaufort's
brother." He paused and let his gaze roam over her.
"You are Heather Carmichael, aren't you?" He
sounded uncertain.

"Yes, sir, I am. I'm here to see Mrs. Beaufort about
the position of nanny to her daughter."

He nodded. "I know, but Jocelyn was called away.
I'll handle the interview." Again he hesitated and
looked at her, letting his glance rest on her face. After
a moment he blinked and brought his attention back
to the open folder. "Forgive me for staring," he said,
"but I find it hard to believe that you're thirty-one
years old."

Heather's eyes widened. "Thirty-one? I'm not
thirty-one, I'm twenty-one."

He frowned. "Then why did you put thirty-one on
your application?" he asked crisply.

"But I didn't.... Please, may I see that?"

He handed the paper to her, and sure enough, in
the space next to "age" was typed a three and a one.
She squirmed with embarrassment. "Oh, dear. It must
have been a typo. I'm sorry. Does it make a difference?"

"I think it well might," he said impatiently. "Ten

years is a long age span. We'd better go over this and make sure there are no more little surprises."

She felt like a child being scolded. How could she have been so careless? They'd had several classes at school on how to apply for a position, one on writing a résumé, another on filling out an application and still another on how to conduct oneself during an interview. She'd just botched all of them!

She nodded agreement and handed the application back to him, and he started reading from it. "All right, we've established your name and age. You've got 'sex' marked right, female."

Heather blushed.

"You have an A.A. degree in early childhood education from Macon, Georgia, community college," he continued, "and graduated last week from the Peachtree Nanny College in Atlanta?"

She nodded.

"You have the required physical examination and clearance, plus the immunization shots?"

Again she nodded.

He scanned a few lines. "I see you've listed your next of kin as an aunt who lives in California. Don't you have any family closer than that?"

This time she shook her head. "No, Aunt Carrie is my mother's older sister, but I hardly know her."

"Where are your parents?" His tone was gentler.

She'd hoped he wouldn't ask that question. "My mother died of cancer when I was twelve, and my father was killed in an automobile accident a year ago." She heard the anguish that always crept into her voice when she talked about her father's death.

"I'm sorry," he said softly.

She ducked her head and hoped he hadn't seen her pain. "Thank you. I guess you know how it feels to lose your father."

"Yes, I do," he said sadly. "When mine died a few years ago it left an aching void in my life. It's filled in somewhat with time, but there'll always be an emptiness."

She looked at him and nodded, feeling oddly comforted. "Yes, that's how I feel, empty and alone."

For a moment they sat in silence, then he cleared his throat. "Well, I guess everything else is in order." His tone was once more businesslike. "However, since you're so much younger than my sister and her husband were led to believe, I can't approve you for employment. You'll have to talk to one or both of them."

Heather's spirits sank. She wasn't sure she wanted the job, but she didn't want to be turned down for it, either. Besides, she had all her things packed and ready to be shipped to Boston.

"Will Mrs. Beaufort be back soon?"

He shook his head. "She won't be back in the office today at all, but they're expecting you at the house. Jocelyn and Franchot were so impressed with your credentials and recommendations that they'd arranged for you to move right in. They'll be there for dinner and you'll have all evening to get acquainted. If it works out, you'll settle in as planned; if not, you'll stay the night and we'll arrange for you to catch a flight back to Atlanta tomorrow."

He glanced at his watch. "If you don't mind waiting around for an hour or so I'll drive you to the house. Or if you'd rather, Nick can take you now. Mother's there—you could visit with her.''

The last thing Heather wanted was to go alone to the Sheffield home and introduce herself to the formidable Daphne Titus Sheffield, daughter of a former secretary of the interior, and widow of a former senator from Massachusetts who was also chairman of the powerful finance committee. The matriarch of the Sheffield family was rumored to be imperialistic and ruthless.

''I...I'd rather wait and go with you,'' she answered promptly.

He stood. ''Fine. If you'd like to do some sightseeing, Faneuil Hall and the Quincy Market are just down the street. Be back here at five-thirty. I should be ready to leave by then.''

Quincy Market wasn't hard to find. It was ablaze with the colorful blossoms, fruits and vegetables that were sold from carts on the cobblestone plaza surrounding the two-hundred-plus-year-old Faneuil Hall, which was familiarly known as the cradle of liberty. The three-story brick building had served as a meeting hall for many stirring meetings during the Revolutionary movement, and British officers had used it as a theater during the occupation of the city.

Heather's keen sense of history was outraged to find that now the entire lower floor had been converted into a circus of fast-food stalls, and she quickly sought refuge in the museum upstairs.

When she returned to the Sheffield office suite, she found Maxwell talking to the receptionist. He looked up and smiled. ''Ah, there you are. Did you have a nice time?''

Heather smiled back. "Yes, Mr. Sheffield, but I didn't mean to keep you waiting."

He picked up his briefcase. "You didn't, Heather, and call me Max. If you mention Mr. Sheffield around here, you'll get any one of us." He took her hand and tucked it in the bend at his elbow. "If you're ready, the car should be at the curb when we get down there."

She liked the way her name sounded when he said it. The Boston accent was unique, although he probably thought the same about her Southern one.

She also liked the solid warmth of his rib cage against her arm. His flesh was firm and muscular.

Although they didn't talk, he continued to hold her arm against him as they rode down in the elevator and walked across the lobby on their way out. A shiny black Jaguar was parked at the curb, and the parking attendant standing next to it opened the door when he saw them coming.

"Good afternoon, Mr. Sheffield," he said, and nodded to her as Max helped her get in and settled on the red leather upholstery.

He thanked the young man who looked to be about Heather's age, then slid into the driver's seat and buckled his seat belt.

The engine turned over with hardly a sound and purred contentedly as Max guided the luxurious beauty through the winding, congested streets. Heather felt like Cinderella, and wondered how long it would be before her coach turned into a pumpkin and she found herself back in Atlanta relying on her two feet to take her places.

It was only a few minutes before they pulled up to

another curb and parked in front of a four-story brick row house that fronted on an uneven cobblestone sidewalk across from a large grassy park. The street-lights were the old-fashioned glass-and-wrought-iron type like those of the gaslight area.

It was altogether charming, and suddenly Heather realized where they were. She caught her breath. "This must be Beacon Hill," she said, mentioning the most prestigious residential area in Boston.

Max grinned. "It is." He motioned to the grounds across from them. "That's the Boston Common. It's the oldest public park in the United States."

Heather knew all about the Boston Common. It was fifty acres of land in the heart of the city that had been set aside by the early Puritans for use as a cow pasture and training field. "Do they still drill soldiers there?" she asked, then realized what a naive question it was.

Max chuckled. "No, but once a year they bring in a cow to graze in order to fulfill the intent."

"You're kidding," she said with a trace of resentment. She'd been teased enough about her naiveté by the chauffeur.

He sobered and drew a cross over his heart. "Word of honor. If you're still here I'll take you over to watch next time they do it."

She smiled. "Thank you, I'll hold you to it. Do you live here?"

He shook his head. "No, not anymore, but it's the family home. My sister and her husband live here with our mother. My three brothers and I still have free run of the place, though."

He got out of the car and came around to help her.

Max opened the door to the house with his own key and ushered her into a small marble-tiled entryway that led into a large ornate parlor.

"Hey, Mom," he yelled, "where are you?"

A big woman of indeterminate age encased in a wraparound apron came bustling in from the back. "Hold it down, Max," she said in a voice that was almost as loud as his had been. "If you wake the baby that snooty nurse'll make you change her diaper."

He laughed. "Like hell she will. Is Mom here?"

The woman looked upward. "She's in her office. You'll have to go get her yourself; I've got to get my vegetables started. You stayin' for dinner?"

"When did I ever pass up the opportunity to eat your prime rib? I smelled it the minute I stepped inside the house."

She grunted and marched back through the swinging door.

Max turned to Heather with a look of affectionate tolerance. "That was Inga, our housekeeper and resident tyrant. She's been with us so long that she's become part of the family. Keeps us all humble." He turned away. "Sit down, and I'll go fetch Mother. I'll just be a minute." He took the stairs two at a time.

Heather walked over to one of the two matching rose damask sofas and sat down gingerly. Here, as in Max's office, everything looked so expensive. She was almost afraid to walk on the Persian carpet, or touch any of the highly polished antique tables.

She'd never been in a row house before, but she'd often wondered about them. They were all tall and narrow, and she figured there couldn't be more than three or four rooms to a floor. This one had a parlor and a kitchen, and she could see part of a dining room through an open space at the back of the wide stairway on the right, which no doubt went all the way to the top of the building.

She sighed. Everything in Boston was so crowded together. It was that way in some parts of Atlanta, too, but in Georgia, those who could afford it still had room for plantation-type mansions with acres of gardens and rambling homes. They didn't build their houses like rectangular silos divided into four or five parts one on top of the other.

In spite of the crowding and the fast pace of this city, Heather's excitement mounted. Who wouldn't be thrilled at the prospect of working for, and living with, one of the country's foremost families in America's oldest city? And the tantalizing thought of Max Sheffield running in and out all the time made the idea irresistible!

Heather immediately realized that was a dangerous thought and attempted to put it out of her mind as she heard voices from the floor above. She stood when Max and a tall, elegant older woman appeared on the stairs.

Daphne Sheffield was as stunning as her pictures portrayed her. At least five foot eight, she was slim as a model and could easily pass for one of the women over forty who graced the cover of *Lears*, a classy magazine for mature female executives.

Although published reports put her age at seventy-one she looked fifty. Her complexion was creamy, with only a few wrinkles to indicate the passing years. Her hair was white but with a silvery sheen, and she wore it pulled back from her oval face and coifed in a beautifully fashioned twist at the back of her head, accentuating her high, prominent cheekbones.

"Mother," Max said as they crossed the floor to stand in front of her, "this is Heather Carmichael."

Heather put out her hand somewhat timidly. "How do you do, Mrs. Sheffield," she said, and was glad her voice didn't quiver the way her knees were doing.

The older woman took her hand in a firm, nononsense grip. "Miss Carmichael."

Her voice had a melodious depth and had obviously been trained. It was the old "iron hand in the velvet glove" tone, softly feminine but underlined with the force of strength.

Daphne Titus Sheffield was a woman rumored to be schooled in the art of getting her own way and who'd perfected that art with a lifetime of practice.

Heather shivered as Daphne's piercing gaze stabbed her. "My son tells me you've misrepresented your age to us," she said imperiously.

"Mother!" Max protested as Heather's mouth dropped open. "She says it was a typo, and I believe her."

Daphne continued to hold Heather's glance. "Oh? Are you in the habit of making such sloppy mistakes on important papers? Or perhaps you don't feel that being employed by the Sheffield family is reason enough to put forth your best effort."

Chapter Two

Heather's heart sank. If she was turned down as a nanny for the Sheffield family, the word would get around and she'd have trouble getting another really good position.

She shouldn't have been so careless, but still Max and his mother were attaching far too much importance to one small typographical error. It must be obvious to them that she hadn't deliberately lied. She tended to look younger than her twenty-one years; there was no way she could have convinced anyone she was ten years older.

That stabbing gaze of Mrs. Sheffield's made her feel guilty even though she knew she was innocent. She squared her shoulders and forced her gaze to meet and hold the other woman's. "Mrs. Sheffield, I needn't tell you what a position with your family could do for my career. My typing skill is only average. I made an error and I'm sorry, but typing isn't one of the requirements for being a good nanny...."

Daphne Sheffield said nothing, just continued to look at Heather as she faltered, then continued. "I love children and, although I was an only child, I've had lots of experience at caring for them. I earned my spending money from junior high through junior college by baby-sitting, and I was always in demand."

Still no word from the other woman as Heather paused to draw a deep breath. "When my, uh, circumstances changed and I decided not to go on to complete my education at the university, I could have qualified for the job of nanny without further training, but I felt it was important to learn as much as I could about small children and their care. I used what money I had available to enroll in the highest-rated nanny college on the East Coast and spent a year perfecting the skills I already had."

As she spoke, Heather's timidity vanished. Underneath Daphne Sheffield's designer clothes she was endowed the same as other women. The only thing she had that Heather didn't was an overdeveloped ego.

Heather tore her gaze away from the other woman and glanced at Max, who was standing beside her looking slightly stunned. He'd probably never seen anyone stand up to his mother before.

Was he one of those sons who let a strong parent run their lives? For some reason that thought was painfully disillusioning.

"I believe you agreed to pay for my flight back to Atlanta if it was decided I wasn't right for the position," she reminded him, "so if you'll give me a check and call a cab, I'll return to the airport."

Max blinked, but before he could answer, his

mother finally spoke. "I think that's a wise decision...."

Max had been watching the play of emotions on this young woman's face, and he could see how desperately she wanted this job. He knew it was none of his business and he should stay out of it, but there was something so touchingly vulnerable about her. He had the disturbing urge to take her in his arms and shield her from his mother's sharp, hurtful words.

Jamming his hands in his pockets to make sure he didn't do anything so foolish, he tried another tactic. "Oh, come off it, Ma," he snapped. "She's not leaving here until Jocelyn has interviewed her. Yvette's her child, and she and Franchot will decide if Heather is suitable."

Daphne glared at him, but there was fondness in her tone when she spoke. "Maxwell, I should have quit having babies after Jocelyn was born, while I was still ahead." She turned and made her way gracefully up the stairs.

He grinned at Heather. "In case you haven't figured it out, I was born two years after Jocelyn."

The sudden release of tension coaxed an involuntary giggle from her, followed by a hearty laugh with Max joining in.

So she'd been wrong. This Sheffield man wasn't intimidated by his mother or anyone else. That discovery made her very happy.

"Do you want to see the baby?" he asked.

"Oh, yes. I understand she's four months old. Who's been taking care of her since her mother returned to work?"

Max took her arm, and they moved toward the

staircase. "Jocelyn's had a pediatric nurse ever since she brought Yvette home from the hospital. I guess the woman's competent enough, but she's also a pain in the rear. You'd think it was her kid the way she tries to keep everyone away from it. Just watch, she'll try to keep us from going in."

They'd reached the third floor, and Max started up the next section of the staircase when Heather stopped him. "Hold on a minute." She gasped. "Where are we going?"

He looked down at her, and his eyes twinkled. "If you want to work here you have to be prepared to climb stairs. The family rooms are on the first floor, Mom's living quarters on the second, Jocelyn and Franchot's on the third and the nursery suite is on the fourth."

"The fourth floor!" She was only half teasing as she caught her breath. "Do you provide oxygen?"

"No, but there is an elevator at the back of the house if you can't hack the climb." He sighed. "Ah, the younger generation, soft and out of shape. I recommend a good body-building class...."

He paused and looked her over. "Mmm, on second thought there's nothing wrong with your body. Better just concentrate on breathing exercises."

She felt a tingling awareness as his roaming gaze touched on her slender curves. Smiling, he held out his hand. "Come on, just one more flight and you'll be home."

Home. Did that mean he'd use his influence with his sister to help her get the job? Was he already thinking of her as part of the household?

She put her hand in his, and it encompassed hers

in a surprisingly intimate grasp as he walked beside her up the remaining steps.

The fourth floor looked much the same as the second and third, with a hall that ran the width of the house at the top of the stairs and doors opening onto it, but as soon as Heather stepped onto the landing, she knew there was something different here. A warmth. Not as in heat, but like an acceptance. As though this story of the house welcomed her.

She shook her head to dislodge such foolishness. My God, talk about imagination!

"This floor was shut up for years after we kids began to leave home," Max said, obviously not noticing her momentary aberration. "This room—" he nodded to the door in the middle of the wall in front of them "—was mine. It had always been the nursery, and since I was the last, I just stayed there."

He put his hand on the knob and turned it. "Now it's a nursery again." He opened the door quietly.

The blind on the window was drawn to shut out the late-afternoon sun, but even so, the room was bright and enchanting. The walls were painted white with pastel mauve accents. The gauzy canopy draped at the top of the four-poster maple crib was the same shade of mauve, and so was the carpet.

On one wall was a hand-painted mural featuring the delightful Beatrix Potter storybook animals, and Heather recognized the furnishings in the room as custom designs from one of the top furniture makers.

"Oh, it's absolutely charming," she whispered.

Max grinned. "Yeah, but wait till you get a look at the baby."

He led her across the room to the crib, and Heather

understood immediately what he'd meant. The baby girl lying there looked as if she could have been custom designed like everything else in the room.

She was a pink-and-white butterball with wide-open, bright blue eyes, a sprinkling of golden hair on her perfectly shaped head and a toothless smile that lit up her flawless cherubic face. She was wearing a short pink ruffled dress with matching ruffled panties, and her chubby little arms and legs were all waving at once.

Heather actually squealed with delight. "Oh, Max, she's beautiful!"

Max gazed at the child with tenderness. "Yes, she is." He sounded like a proud father as he leaned over and picked her up, careful to support her head. "Hi there, cutie," he crooned. "Got a kiss for Uncle Max?"

He kissed her on the forehead and cradled her in the crook of his arm as he spoke. "What are you so happy about? I'll bet you just had your bottle, didn't you?"

He chucked her under her double chin, and the smile widened as her arms and legs pumped back and forth with glee.

He looked at Heather. "Would you like to hold her?"

Would she! Her arms ached for the privilege. "I'd love to," she said eagerly, "but will it be all right with the nurse?" She looked around. "Where is she?"

He expertly flipped the baby over his shoulder and rubbed her back. "Probably in her room. She must not have heard us come up," he said as he put the child in her arms.

Yvette was heavier than Heather had expected, and she smelled faintly of milk and baby powder. She snuggled contentedly into Heather's arms, and the big blue eyes fastened their gaze on her face as one small fist found its way to the petallike mouth.

As she murmured nonsense to the precious burden she held, Heather knew she'd do anything to get this position of nanny. Everything about it felt so right, as though she'd been preordained to come to Boston and be a part of the Sheffield family.

As soon as the thought took form, she knew the idea was preposterous. Even if she were hired as a nanny, she wouldn't be a part of the famous family. She'd be an employee, and she'd better not forget that.

It would be so easy to settle in here and hope for more, especially from Max, but that way led to heartbreak, and she'd had all of that she could cope with.

A gasp from behind them brought both Heather and Max to attention, and they turned as one to be confronted by a matronly woman in a white uniform.

"Mr. Sheffield." There was outrage in her tone. "I've asked you to check in with me before you come to see the baby. Now you've wakened her and thrown her off schedule."

She turned her withering gaze on Heather. "And I can't have you bringing in people off the street to handle the poor child and expose her to illness."

Heather felt like a plague carrier and cringed as she hugged Yvette to her, but Max returned the woman's hostility with the chilling voice of authority. "Let's get one thing straight, madam," he said in the same "iron in velvet" tone as his mother's. "I don't need your permission to see my niece, day or night, and anyone I bring up here is a special guest who will be treated with the utmost respect. Is that clear?"

Taken separately, none of his words could be construed as hostile or threatening, but put together with the aura of power surrounding him and the menace in his quiet voice, his meaning was unmistakable. *No one intimidates a Sheffield.*

Even the officious nurse blanched, but she stood her ground. "I'm sorry if I was abrupt," she said, not sounding at all contrite, "but the child is my responsibility. I'll have to speak to Mrs. Beaufort about your continued disregard of my wishes."

"You do that," Max said icily, and the nurse turned abruptly and stalked out of the room.

After they'd played with the baby for a while, they started back downstairs, but were met on the third floor by a young version of Daphne Sheffield coming through the broad archway of a room to the right of them and across the hall. A glimpse of the furnishings revealed it to be a parlor.

Heather knew this was Max's sister even before he introduced them. She was tall and slim like her mother, but her hair was a stunning shade of blond.

"Hello, Heather," Jocelyn Beaufort said pleasantly as the two women shook hands. "Mother tells me there's been a mix-up about your age." Her glance roamed over the younger woman. "Not that I wouldn't have seen it for myself. You'd never pass for thirty-one." She glanced up the stairway. "I just got home and was going up to look in on my little daughter, but if you'd like to go in and keep my husband company—'' she waved toward the room she'd just left ''—I'll be back in a few minutes and we'll talk about it.''

She turned her attention to her brother. ''Are you staying, Max?''

He grinned. ''Unless you kick me out. I hope you decide to keep Heather. I've had about all I can stomach of that nurse.''

Jocelyn chuckled. ''Step on your ego, did she?''

Max took a playful swipe at his sister's derriere, which she easily sidestepped. ''Just get rid of her, okay,'' he called as she ran up the stairs laughing.

Heather felt a keen regret that she'd never had a sister or brother.

As they walked into the sitting room, a good-looking man standing behind the bar in the corner pouring whiskey from a cut-crystal decanter greeted them. ''Hi. Come on in and have a drink. Jocelyn's up in the nursery but she'll be down shortly.''

''We ran in to her in the hall,'' Max replied. ''Franchot, this is Heather Carmichael. Heather, Franchot's the baby's father.''

The dark-haired man laughed as he reached across the bar to take Heather's hand. ''See what becoming a father does to you.'' He spoke in a teasing moan, but his brown eyes twinkled. ''I used to be known as Franchot Beaufort, stockbroker *extraordinaire*. Now I'm just 'the baby's father.'''

Heather laughed. ''We've just come from the nursery and, for what it's worth, your little Yvette is more beautiful than any stock certificate I've ever seen.''

"Bless you, my child," he murmured piously. "Now what'll you have to drink?"

Heather asked for a cola, and Max said he'd have scotch on the rocks.

"So you're the nanny," Franchot commented as they settled themselves on the comfortable contemporary furniture in the brown, beige and green room. "I understand there's been a glitch in the plans. Something about your age?"

Heather explained what had happened. "It was such a stupid error," she concluded, "but I really do want this position. I might not be much of a typist, but I'm a very good nanny."

Franchot contemplated his glass. "I'm sure you are, but I'll have to tell you that if you'd put your true age on the application we'd never have considered you. You're little more than a child yourself."

Heather's hopes plummeted. It probably did seem that way to him. Franchot looked to be in his early forties and old enough to be her father. Her own father had only been forty-three when he'd been killed.

The thought of her dad as she'd last seen him, broken and bleeding, brought tears to her eyes, and she was relieved when Jocelyn returned just then and fixed Max with a disapproving glare. "Dammit, Max, why did you have to get the nurse all stirred up? Now she's threatening to quit?"

"Good!" Max said. "What's your problem? She was leaving anyway as soon as you found a nanny."

"But that's just it," Jocelyn said anxiously. "We haven't found a nanny yet—" She broke off when she caught sight of Heather. "Oh, that is...we still don't know..." She gave up and headed for the bar. "I need a drink," she muttered.

Heather repeated to Jocelyn and Franchot all the things she'd told Max and his mother about her education, experience and qualifications. "You've read my references," she said in conclusion, "and Peachtree college guarantees satisfaction or they'll furnish a replacement. Please, won't you give me a month on probation? Then if you feel I'm too immature for the job you can fire me."

Franchot and Jocelyn looked at each other, and Max smiled at her encouragingly, but before anyone could speak again a sound not unlike a doorbell chimed.

Franchot sighed and put down his empty glass. "That means dinner's ready," he announced, and looked at Heather. "Jocelyn and I will discuss this and give you our decision in the morning. Your suitcase has been put in the guest bedroom on the fourth floor. Jocelyn will take you up and see that you're settled later. Right now we'd better go downstairs. Inga gets testy if we aren't all seated when she brings in the food."

Dinner with the Sheffield family was an experience Heather would treasure even if she didn't get the job. It was a gourmet meal served on exquisite bone china and eaten with ornate sterling-silver place settings. The furnishings in the dining room were priceless mahogany antiques, and the tablecloth was fine white linen.

Most of the conversation went right over her head. It was concentrated on family matters, politics and the law practice. She spoke only when spoken to, and noticed that the nurse did the same. Mrs. Sheffield had introduced the two women, but they had little to say to each other, although they were seated together on one side of the table.

When the meal was over, the nurse excused herself and returned to the nursery, leaving Heather confused and wondering what her next move should be. It had been a long, exciting day and she was exhausted. She'd wakened that morning in Atlanta, and would go to sleep tonight in Boston. Although the two cities were in the same time zone she still felt disoriented. Probably culture shock rather than jet lag, but she had a nagging need to get away by herself where she could relax.

As they filed out of the dining room she caught up with Jocelyn. "Excuse me, Mrs. Beaufort," she said politely, "but if you don't mind I'd like to go to my room now. If you'll tell me where it is I can find it by myself—"

A familiar voice from behind her interrupted. "I'll show her," Max said, and took her arm. "After all, I was delegated the official greeter."

Jocleyn's eyebrows rose slightly. "Well, if you don't mind..." She lowered her voice. "Watch it, brother dear. I only asked you to interview her, nothing was said about putting her to bed."

Heather's eyes widened, and her breath seemed caught in her diaphragm. Max muttered a short, crude oath and verbally tore into his sister. "For God's sake, try to remember that you're supposed to be a lady. Heather's not used to your twisted sense of humor."

"It wasn't meant to be funny," she snapped, then

looked at Heather. "But I didn't mean to offend you, Heather. I'm afraid I spoke before I realized how it would sound. If you want to work for us, though, you'd better get used to that. The Sheffield siblings are great teasers. Now sleep well, and I'll see you at breakfast no later than eight in the morning."

She walked away, and Max and Heather went upstairs.

Once again, as they stepped onto the fourth-floor landing, she was aware of the soothing warmth that surrounded her, and also as before, Max seemed unaware of the phenomenon. She tried to ignore it as they turned to the right and stopped in front of the third door on the wall.

Max opened it, then turned on the light and stepped back to allow her to enter. It was a pretty room, with a window onto the back and expensive furnishings.

The bed covers were turned back, and her nightgown and robe were laid neatly across them. Her astonishment must have shown because Max opened the closet door to reveal the few clothes she'd brought hanging inside. "One of the maids unpacked for you," he explained.

"Oh, dear," she said with a sigh. "She should have waited. I'll probably just have to pack again in the morning."

"Maybe not." His tone was gentle. "Would it make you feel any better if I told you that I'd be happy to have you looking after my children if I had any?"

She managed a sad smile. "Thank you, it does make me feel better. What a shame that you don't have some."

He nodded. "Yes, it is. I'd like to have a family. Lots of little sons and daughters. My mother has fourteen grandchildren. I'm the only one who hasn't contributed."

The idea of Max Sheffield's children intrigued Heather. There was a strong family resemblance between the members she'd met so far, so his kids would probably look like him, but they could deviate enough to have black hair and blue eyes....

Don't be an idiot, she scolded herself. *You're dreaming of mixing your genes with Max's, and that will never happen. Get real!*

She pulled her thoughts back to the present, then stammered when she tried to speak. "You...you have a lot of time yet."

"Yes, but I'd like to have them while I'm still young enough to play with them." He sounded as though he were thinking out loud. "My brother, Titus, was married while still in college. He was a young father, and now he's a young grandfather. I'm thirty years old and still haven't found a woman I'd want to spend the rest of my life with."

Heather didn't need to be told that the elder brother, Titus, whom Max spoke of, was a U.S. congressman and head of the House Ways and Means Committee, which made him a man with much influence in the nation's capital.

She didn't know what to say to such personal revelations, and for a moment they were both silent. Then Max snapped out of his reverie and grinned. "Good grief, I'm getting maudlin in my old age. I'm sorry."

He looked around the room, and when he spoke

again his tone was impersonal. "The bathroom's across the hall, and the telephone has both in-house and outside lines. If you need anything just ring the housekeeper's number and Inga will take care of it." He hesitated. "I...I'll say goodbye now and hope it's just temporary."

He put out his hand and Heather took it. Again his touch sent tingles up her arm. "Goodbye, and thank you." She didn't sound nearly as businesslike as he had. "I hope it's temporary, too, but if not...well, it's been very nice meeting you."

His tender gaze held hers. "I wouldn't have missed it," he said softly, and squeezed her hand. "*Au revoir,* Heather."

Heather slept soundly all night and woke up disoriented, until she remembered where she was. A glance at her watch told her it was only six-thirty. She had plenty of time to dress and get down to breakfast.

She stretched and burrowed deeper into the comfortable mattress. Would this be the only time she'd ever spend the night in this house? That probability was a distressing one. Beacon Hill would be a great place to live and work, and the baby was such a little doll.

Just then the "little doll" in the next room let out a yowl that was guaranteed to wake anyone on the floor. Heather's first instinct was to jump out of bed and hurry into the nursery to see what was the matter, but as she was reaching for her robe, she remembered that the nurse was the one in charge and it wasn't likely that she'd welcome Heather's interference.

Yvette continued to cry lustily, and a few moments later Heather heard footsteps on the beautiful hardwood floor in the hall, then the nursery door opened and closed. Almost immediately the child stopped crying.

Although Heather could hear the murmur of a voice, she couldn't make out what was being said as she put on her robe and went across the hall to the bathroom. While showering she let herself dare to believe that the Beauforts would change their minds and decide she was the nanny they wanted for their tiny daughter, after all.

At Peachtree college she'd been taught that a nanny dresses conservatively when starting a new position until she learns what is expected, so she'd brought her meager supply of skirts and blouses with her. The three outfits could be mixed and matched to make it appear that she had more than she did.

This morning she chose a red linen-weave skirt and a red-and-white striped blouse that accentuated the natural color in her cheeks and lifted her spirits. When she got to the bottom of the stairway she heard voices coming from the dining room and took a deep breath to steady her quivering nerves.

As she walked to the open doorway she realized there was an argument going on, but by then it was too late to retreat since Mrs. Sheffield, who was sitting at the head of the table, had seen her.

"Come in, Miss Carmichael," she said. "We were just discussing you."

Oh, dear, Heather thought as she advanced and looked at the people sitting around the table. The Beauforts were both there, and so was Max! What was he doing here so early? He'd distinctly told her that he didn't live at the family home anymore.

Max and Franchot stood, and all three greeted her. "Breakfast is set up buffet-style on the sideboard," Mrs. Sheffield said, indicating the row of covered serving dishes on the chest against the wall. "You may help yourself."

The aroma of bacon, eggs and fresh-baked pastry was mouth watering, but Heather was too tense to eat. She passed up the food and poured herself a cup of coffee to take to the table. Jocelyn motioned to the chair beside her and Heather sat down.

Max eyed her coffee cup. "Aren't you going to eat? It's quite a while until lunch."

Now everyone was looking at her, and her tension increased. "The food smells delicious," she said nervously, "but I'm really not hungry."

"Did you sleep well?" he asked, and sounded as if he really cared.

"Oh, yes, thank you. I dozed right off and didn't wake up until I heard the baby cry at six-thirty." She hesitated a moment, then blurted, "I'm surprised to see you here this morning. Didn't you say you have your own home?"

He looked a little sheepish. "Yes, I do, but I stayed here last night."

"She's got a point," Jocelyn commented. "What *are* you doing here so early in the morning? This is the first time you've had breakfast with us in months."

"Well, pardon me." Max sounded offended. "I didn't realize I was supposed to get your permission to spend a night at the family home."

Heather was sorry she'd brought up the subject. She wished they'd quit bickering and tell her what they'd decided about her. Didn't they know how much this job meant to her? Surely even the superrich knew that the average person had to work in order to live.

Finally it was Franchot who cut through the quibbling. "Heather, I'm sure you're anxious to hear our decision about you so I'll get right to the point. I'm sorry but Mrs. Beaufort and I feel that we need an older, more mature woman to care for our child. Since the Sheffield family is in the limelight so much we have special problems with security, et cetera, that would be difficult for a girl your age to handle."

Heather had expected as much, but still the disappointment was both painful and frightening. The money from her dad's small insurance policy was almost gone, and she needed a job immediately.

"But, Mr. Beaufort," she interrupted, unable to accept dismissal without at least trying to convince them. "I'm a very competent nanny. The college wouldn't have recommended me if I hadn't been."

"My dear, we've never doubted that." Franchot sounded sincere. "You're also a delightful young lady, and we'd enjoy having you as a member of the household. This has been a difficult decision, but I'm afraid we must stand by it."

Heather knew she'd lost. It would do no good to argue. The Beauforts knew what they wanted and it wasn't her. She wondered how much influence Mrs. Sheffield had had in their decision. Would the parents have been willing to take a chance on her if the grandmother hadn't been so opposed?

She stole a glance across the table at Max. He was looking at her with a mixture of sympathy and anger. Was it possible that he'd argued with them in her favor?

She blinked back tears of disappointment, and was appalled when one trickled down her cheek. All the Beauforts' doubts about her maturity would be confirmed if she broke down and cried!

She swallowed and pressed her lips together to keep them from trembling, but before she could speak Jocelyn reached out and patted Heather's hand. "Now that you understand that we can't offer you a permanent position, Franchot and I are hoping you'll forgive us enough to help us out of a really desperate bind."

Heather's eyes widened with surprise. How could she possibly help them?

"The nurse received word late last night that her mother, who lives in Santa Fe, has had a stroke and is in critical condition," Jocelyn continued. "She's leaving on the first flight out at ten-thirty, and we have no one to replace her until we can find a permanent nanny. Would you consider taking the position on a temporary basis until—"

"Dammit, Jocelyn, you're using her," Max accused, much to Heather's amazement. "If you trust her enough to take her on temporarily, why not give her a chance at the job permanently? Do as she suggested and put her on probation for a month. If it doesn't work out you can always let her go."

"Now look, Max," Franchot snapped. "We've been over this with you already, and I thought you understood our feelings. Why should it matter to you, anyway? It's my child who's involved, and I cannot agree to putting a schoolgirl in charge of her care and upbringing.''

"Oh, for God's sake, Franchot, Heather's not a schoolgirl." Max threw down his napkin and stood. "Take a look at her. She's a full-grown woman. Just because she's younger than you expected doesn't mean she's not fully competent. She's a hell of a lot more sensible than that woman you've got now—"

"Maxwell!" Mrs. Sheffield didn't raise her voice in order to be heard, but there was a sting in her tone that silenced everybody, including a livid Max.

"I think we've heard quite enough from you," she said. "Franchot is right, this is none of your concern. I can't imagine why you're making such a fuss."

She made a point of looking at her watch. "It's getting late. If you have an early appointment at the office, we'll excuse you, otherwise sit down and be quiet."

Heather sat through this exchange in stunned silence. She'd hoped Max might argue in her favor, but she'd never expected him to be so vehement about it.

With a glance of apology at Heather, he sat down, and his mother looked at him with affection. "Thank you, my dear," she said softly, then turned to Jocelyn. "Please continue."

Jocelyn nodded. "As I was saying, Heather, would you stay on temporarily for a few days until Peachtree college can supply us with another applicant. It seems that all their graduates for this term have been placed, but they're contacting some of their alumni who may be looking for a change."

Heather's emotions ranged from happiness to despair. If she accepted the temporary position she would have the opportunity to show the Beauforts what a capable nanny she was, and maybe they'd let her stay, after all. On the other hand, by telling the college that she wasn't acceptable, they'd severely damaged her chance of being accepted by anyone else.

There was only one answer Heather could give. "I'm sorry I don't meet your qualifications, but I'd be happy to stay until you find someone more suitable, or until the college finds me another position, whichever comes first."

Jocelyn and Franchot thanked her and expressed their pleasure, and Mrs. Sheffield seemed relieved that the matter was settled. Only Max was still upset, and he said nothing until they were all leaving the table.

Then he caught up with Heather and took her arm. "Walk out to the car with me," he urged, and led her through the kitchen and out into the backyard where his Jaguar was parked in the driveway behind the garage.

"I'm sorry for the way my pigheaded family has treated you," he said. "I used all the arguments I could think of to get them to hire you, but..." He shrugged. "You can see how much influence I have."

She was just happy that he'd cared enough to make the effort. Turning to face him, she smiled. "Max, it's all right. You'll understand better when you have a child of your own. Jocelyn is in her mid-thirties, and Franchot is old enough to be my father. They think of me as still a kid, and they feel that I'm not old enough to be entrusted with the Beaufort-Sheffield heir."

His gaze searched her face. "They didn't see you with that baby. The way your eyes lit up when you looked at her, the confident but tender way you held her and the way she seemed to understand all the nonsense you were talking to her and loving every word of it."

Heather laughed lightly. "Of course she did. I was telling her what a gorgeous baby she is."

He put his hand under her chin and tilted her face up. His eyes were dark with emotion. "It takes one to know one." His tone was gentle. "You must have been a little angel, because you grew up to be so breathtakingly beautiful."

His gaze settled on her mouth, and she swayed toward him as her heart missed a beat and her bones turned liquid. His hands closed around her shoulders, and she watched as his face moved slowly down until his lips touched hers.

Her breath caught, and she seemed to hear the far-off strains of music too heavenly to be real as his mouth moved over hers, then lifted to touch briefly each closed eyelid before he stepped back and dropped his hands.

"I won't let them send you away," he murmured, then turned and got into the car.

Heather was still standing there listening to the nonexistent symphony long after he drove off.

Chapter Three

After a hurried conference with Heather to acquaint her with the baby's schedule, the nurse left to catch her plane, and Heather took over the full-time care of little Yvette.

The child proved to be as happy and content as she'd appeared, and for the next three days everything went smoothly—with two exceptions. Heather hadn't seen nor heard from Max since he'd captivated her with that feathery kiss, and there was something definitely strange about the fourth-floor sitting room.

It was a cozy parlor situated in the area to the left as one came up the stairway, across the hall from the master bedroom. Unlike the other rooms in the nineteenth-century home that were an elegant blend of French and English antiques interspersed with American contemporary, this one was furnished entirely in American colonial decor. A sparse, austere setting that seemed out of place in company with the more luxurious embellishment of the rest of the house.

But it wasn't only the furnishings that made the room strange. It was the atmosphere.

The feelings of warmth and acceptance that had radiated in the hallway on the fourth floor were magnified in the living room. They'd hit her with almost physical force the minute she'd first stepped through the archway, and she'd been aware of them every time she'd entered the room since.

At first it had unsettled her, but since neither the nurse nor Jocelyn seemed to notice anything amiss, Heather hadn't mentioned it. Still it was odd. Why was she the only one who seemed to be affected by this phenomenon?

Then there was Jocelyn's puzzling revelation on that first day when she'd taken Heather on a tour of the house, starting at the basement and ending in the master bedroom on the fourth floor. It was a very feminine room with Victorian furnishings and a private bathroom, and Heather had praised it lavishly.

"I love the delicate blue-and-gray striped wallpaper," she'd said in conclusion, "and the darker blue of the flowered bedspread and curtains blends so well. Did you do the decorating?"

"Yes, I did," Jocelyn had answered, surprising Heather. Most wealthy women hired professional decorators. "When we decided to open this floor again for the nursery I wanted to try my hand at doing it myself. I was getting along just fine until I came to the sitting room."

She paused for a moment as though remembering, then spoke in a barely audible voice. "I just don't know what got into me."

Heather had already been shown the room, but she

hadn't commented on its quaintness. Now Jocelyn had given her an opening. "I noticed that it's very different from the softer, more cozy decor of the rest of the floor, but it's truly unique. Why, some of that furniture must be museum quality."

Jocelyn nodded. "It is. Franchot positively roared when he got the bills. That maple secretary was hand-made in 1774, and the hickory-and-maple Windsor armchair is even older." She became more agitated as she spoke and finally threw up her hands in disgust. "The point is that I don't even like the furniture of that period. It's stark and uncomfortable, and to my mind downright ugly."

Heather stared at the other woman in amazement. If she didn't like it, why did she buy it? It sounded like a rather impertinent question so she didn't ask. "I'm sure it was a good investment," she said, instead.

"Oh, sure," Jocelyn agreed. "But I'm not a collector, and valuable as it is, it's still out of place up here with all the fluff and whimsy of a nursery."

Heather was hopelessly confused. "I don't understand," she confessed. "If you don't like it, and didn't want it as an investment, then why did you choose it for that particular room?"

The look on Jocelyn's face was a study of perplexity, with just a trace of fear. "I don't know." Her tone was as bewildered as her expression. "I was going to do it in Victorian, like this room, but I found the settee in the attic. I remembered it being in my grandmother's house when I was a child. It was a family heirloom from the 1700s so I decided to use it."

She looked around nervously, then sat down on the blue velvet upholstered chair. Heather sat across from her on the bottom of the bed as Jocelyn continued. "I had it reupholstered with springs and thick batting under the wine velvet covering and put in the parlor. Although it was older, it fit in with the style of the late 1800s, which was what I had in mind. The problem started when I began shopping for the rest of the furnishings. I'd see something that was just what I had in mind, but when it was brought into the room it was all wrong and I'd have to send it back."

She shivered and rubbed her arms with her hands. "It was eerie, and I still get a chill when I think of it. Then one day I went to a private auction. That's where I found that monstrous secretary. I suddenly had the oddest feeling that it was exactly what I needed for the parlor. I didn't even like the damn thing, but I joined the bidding and bought it. When it was delivered it fit that space against the wall between the two built-in bookcases exactly."

This time it was Heather who shivered. There really was something unnatural about that room! She considered telling Jocelyn about her almost psychic impression of the whole floor, but it was too nebulous to put into words. How could she describe feelings that had no basis in fact?

Jocelyn shook her head as though to clear it. "After that, I gave up and shopped for American colonial. I'm embarrassed to say that I came to think of it as almost preordained, and now I'm stuck with it."

The story had haunted Heather every time she entered the sitting room after that and felt the indescribable warm embrace of welcome that surged around her.

By Saturday Heather had been in Boston five days, and she was getting used to life with the fabulous Sheffield family. Too used to it, since it was only a temporary stopover.

She kept telling herself not to get deeply attached to the baby, but it was already too late. That little charmer had wound her tiny fist around Heather's heart that very first day and wouldn't let go. She loved every minute she spent with the child, and Yvette grinned and chortled every time Heather came near her.

She also spent a lot of time in the sitting room, even though the furniture in her bedroom was more comfortable. She was getting used to the welcoming parlor, and it no longer made her uneasy. Instead she sought it out. She never felt alone or lonely in that room, although she was more apt to think about her father there.

The memories didn't make her sad, though. They were happy recollections that made her feel closer to him. Such as all those nights when he'd read bedtime stories to her, and that spring when she was eleven and he'd gone with her to the Camp Fire Girls mother-daughter tea because Mama wasn't feeling well enough to go. Neither of them had known then that Mama would be dead in less than a year.

She'd been so content that she'd unwisely let her guard down and wasn't prepared for the shock she received when Jocelyn sought her out that bright and sunny Saturday afternoon.

The baby was taking her nap, and Heather was reading and listening to Bon Jovi's new release when Jocelyn appeared in the archway of the parlor. "Am I interrupting you?" she asked.

Heather put down her book. "No, not at all. Just let me turn off the stereo."

She started to get up, but Jocelyn stopped her. "That's not necessary. I like Bon Jovi."

For a few moments they listened to the music. The sound was turned down low so as not to wake Yvette, and Jocelyn didn't have to raise her voice to be heard when she spoke again. "Heather, I hate to have to tell you this but the school has found us another nanny."

Heather caught her breath as surprise and dismay hit her with twin blows. "So soon?"

Jocelyn nodded. "Yes. It was a stroke of luck. The woman has been with a family in New York for a couple of years, but now their children no longer need a nanny so Miss Zimmerman was looking for another position."

Heather was devastated. Now she'd never have a chance to prove her competency to these people, but even more painful, her friendship with Max would be terminated before it had really begun.

"Then you won't be needing me anymore."

Nothing like voicing the obvious, she berated herself. Would she ever be sophisticated enough to think up sparkling repartee when her heart was breaking?

Jocelyn looked uncomfortable. "I'm sorry," she said gently. "We've truly enjoyed having you with us these past few days, and I'll write you a glowing reference. If you were only a little older..."

"I know," Heather said, not wanting the conversation to become emotional. "When will Mrs. Zimmerman take over?"

Jocelyn smiled. "It's *Miss* Zimmerman. She's thirty-eight and never been married. The school assures us that her qualifications are impeccable, and she's coming for a personal interview on Monday. If everything works out she'll move in the following weekend."

There wasn't much to say after that, and Jocelyn left a short time later. Heather leaned her head back and closed her eyes, letting the feelings of banishment and defeat wash over her and making a determined effort not to cry.

For a little while she was too lost in her own misery to notice anything else, but gradually she realized that she wasn't alone. Someone else was in the room!

But that was impossible. She hadn't heard anybody come up the stairs, and the hallway was uncarpeted. She'd surely have heard footsteps!

Opening her eyes, she stared straight ahead at the archway, then across the hall, through the open door and into her bedroom.

There was no one there.

Still she felt the presence of someone other than herself. Could it be Max playing games with her? She turned her head to the left, then the right, and finally got out of the chair and turned around to look behind her.

There was no other person in the room, so why did she have the feeling of being watched?

The back of her neck tingled, and she whirled

around. It must be someone teasing her but, as before, the room was empty except for herself.

She sank back down into the chair and shuddered. Dear Lord, what was the matter with her?

Taking a deep breath, she tried to relax. This was ridiculous. She wasn't the type to have an anxiety attack. It was probably the old house. Built in the mid-1800s it had been meticulously kept up, but even so, there were the usual creaks and groans that are inevitable in aged wood, plaster and brick.

The building had character. Heather had heard it settling around her in the quiet of the nights, and the noises had never been frightening.

She felt her tight nerves ease and closed her eyes. The tape player had shut itself off, and the room was peaceful and quiet.

She was just beginning to doze when a soft male voice spoke. "Mistress Heather, be not distressed. You will not be sent away."

Still drifting in the peaceful void between sleeping and waking, Heather opened her eyes. The room seemed hazy, but she could make out the figure of a tall, slender man standing in front of the secretary to her left, not more than four or five steps away from her.

It definitely was not Max!

She was startled, but couldn't wake up enough to be afraid. There was nothing threatening about him as he stood there dressed in a white full-sleeved shirt open at the throat, and black knee-length trousers that buckled over long white stockings.

He was apparently in costume, although his long hair tied back at the nape wasn't too unusual. Some guys in their late teens and early twenties still let their hair grow, but this man was much older. The lines in his face could only have been earned with time and anguish.

"Who are you?" she asked.

"Ethan Hadleigh," he answered simply.

She tried to sit up straight, but her muscles wouldn't respond. "Were you here a few minutes ago?"

"Aye."

"Then why didn't you say something, and where were you?"

"I was right here, but I didn't want to frighten you."

She blinked and the mist cleared. He hadn't moved or even gestured as he spoke, and for the first time Heather was aware that there was something not right about him, but she couldn't grasp what it was.

"What do you mean you were right here?" she asked testily. "I looked all over and there was no one in this room or the hall. For someone who didn't want to frighten me, you did a bang-up job of it."

"Then I beg your forgiveness," he said. "'Twas not my intention."

His voice was soft and low, and so contrite that she couldn't stay angry. "What are you doing up here?" she asked as she again tried to rouse herself from the lethargy of sleep. "Do you work for the Sheffields?"

"I reside here, but you are welcome..."

A cry from the nursery brought Heather to full wakefulness and out of her chair. For a moment she was still disoriented and glanced around for her visitor, but the room was empty.

It was with both relief and dismay that she realized it had all been a dream.

Dinner with the family that evening was a strain for Heather. She didn't feel like trying to convince Jocelyn and Franchot that she was accepting her dismissal gracefully when she wasn't. She was disappointed and angry. It was unwarranted, possibly even illegal, for them to judge her by age alone!

Since Yvette was wide-awake and playful, Heather took her down and put her in her swing beside the table. When the baby was asleep at mealtimes, Velma, the maid, stayed on the fourth floor with her, but when she was awake, Heather usually brought her to the dining room to be with the family.

Yvette quickly took the spotlight off Heather, and as soon as the meal was over she excused herself and took the baby upstairs to bathe her and put her to bed.

It was still dusk outside when Heather settled down in the sitting room once more. She felt a little silly when she found herself gazing into the shadowed corners for a tall man in a colonial-style costume. The dream had seemed so real!

The dinner lay heavy in her stomach, and her eyes burned from holding back tears that pressed to escape. Crying wouldn't do any good; she'd found that out when her father was killed. Her face had become raw from the frequent tears, but they didn't bring him back. Neither would they secure her position here.

She thought of Max and wondered if he knew she'd be leaving. Surely he did, but he hadn't even bothered to come over and offer sympathy. Obviously that kiss, which had meant so much to her, was just his way of saying goodbye since she hadn't heard from him.

A small sob bubbled up in her throat, but she resolutely swallowed it. No way was she going to anguish over Maxwell Sheffield. Actually, he'd done her a kindness by not carrying their brief attraction any further. Men like him only got involved with women like her as a lark. The mother of those children he wanted would be chosen with care from another old-money New England family who would keep the bloodline pure.

A deeper sob shook her with its intensity. It also released the tears, and they streamed down her cheeks.

"Oh, damn!" she wailed as she curled up in a ball in the middle of the settee with her knees under her chin and her arms hugging her legs.

Burying her face in her knees, she gave up and sobbed noisily. It wasn't fair. She'd lost her mother, then her father, her chance at the perfect job, and as if that weren't enough, the only man she'd ever been strongly attracted to was way out of her league and had only been toying with her.

She'd been so immersed in her self-pitying thoughts that she didn't hear the heavy footsteps coming up the stairs until they bounded onto the hall and turned in her direction. Before she could do more than lift her head, Max strode into the unlit room.

"Heather?" he called, then spotted her. "What on earth are you sitting here in the dusk for?"

He hit the light switch, and that's when he saw her tear-ravaged face. "Oh, baby," he murmured compassionately and, hurrying across the room, sat down beside her and took her in his arms. "Don't cry," he muttered. "The job's not worth it."

Reaching into his back pocket, he took out a handkerchief and dabbed at her wet cheeks. "Here," he said, and handed it to her. "Blow."

She took it and blew her nose, then crumpled it in her hand. "I...I'm sorry," she whispered as he guided her head down to lie on his shoulder. He was wearing a lime-green cashmere pullover sweater that was soft and ticklish under her burning skin.

"You have nothing to be sorry for," he muttered. "I apologize for my thick-headed sister and her husband. I should think they'd want someone young and enthusiastic like you to look after their baby, instead of an old maid who probably doesn't even remember what it's like to be a child."

In spite of her misery Heather couldn't help but smile at his description. "I don't think the term 'old maid' is used much anymore," she told him.

"Oh?" he said, and she felt rather than heard the chuckle in his chest. "How about, 'spinster lady'?"

She giggled. "I think the proper form of address is 'single woman,' and I'm sure she'll be just what your sister is looking for."

That sentiment brought another sob, and Max's arms around her tightened as the tears flowed again. "I wish I'd been here," he said against her hair. "I might have been able to talk them out of this nonsense, but I've been in D.C. for the past couple of days on business and just got home this afternoon. I came over to find out how things were working out for you, and Mother told me about the new nanny."

Heather sobbed quietly against his shoulder. She

wished he could hold her like this forever, warm and safe and protected. He had a fresh, woodsy scent, and the most comfortable chest she'd ever snuggled against. Not that there'd been that many male chests in her life, but none of them had made her heart pound the way it was pounding now.

"What are you going to do?" he asked. "Does the college have another position lined up for you?"

"Not yet," she said with a sniffle. "I guess I'll just go back there and wait for them to place me."

"Don't do that," he said, and lightly caressed her back through the silky blue blouse she wore. "Stay here. I'll help you find a job. It shouldn't be difficult. I know dozens of couples with children, and they're always looking for baby-sitters."

Heather winced. "I'm not a baby-sitter," she said indignantly, "I'm a trained nanny."

Max's hands stilled. "Of course. I didn't mean to downgrade your chosen occupation. It's the terminology that tripped me up. I promise it won't happen again."

She raised her head to look at him. "But that's the problem, don't you see? Parents aren't nearly as careful about whom they hire as a baby-sitter for a few occasional hours as they are about a nanny who will be more or less raising their children. When word gets around that I've been tried and found wanting by the Sheffield family, no one's going to trust me. Especially not in Boston."

She tried to sit up, but he gently pushed her head back down on his shoulder. "Don't pull away from me," he murmured. "I like holding you. It feels so good, and you smell like apple blossoms. I thought of you a lot while I was away.''

"You did?" she asked, surprised by his admission.

"Yes, I did. Have you thought of me at all since we saw each other last?"

Thought of him? She'd hardly thought of anything else, except the baby she'd been caring for, but she couldn't tell him that. He'd think she had an adolescent crush on him.

Maybe she did, but she was afraid her feelings were far more mature than that. She didn't dare hope, though, that his concern for her was anything more than guilt at the way his sister had dismissed her without a fair trial.

"I...I wondered why you didn't come back...uh, I mean...to see your mother," she finished lamely.

"No one told you I was out of town?" He sounded surprised.

"No," she said. "Well...that is...I didn't ask."

He rubbed his cheek against her temple. "Why not?" he whispered into her ear.

His breath tickled the sensitive cavity and sent tingles down her spine. "It was none of my business," she said shakily.

"Of course it was your business if you were interested. I should have called you. I wanted to, but I was afraid you'd think I was coming on too strong." He cleared his throat, then changed the subject. "Will you at least let me make some inquiries?" he asked.

"Inquiries?" Heather couldn't think what he was talking about.

"Query my friends and clients to see if any of them need a modern-day Mary Poppins," he prodded.

"Oh." She'd lost track of their previous conversation. "Yes, I'd be most grateful if you would. I'll be here for another week. Mrs. Beaufort said that Miss Zimmerman will be moving in next weekend, so I'll probably leave here on Saturday morning."

His hands moved caressingly over her back again. "Don't forget, she hasn't been hired yet. She still has the personal interview to get through. Now tell me, do you have tomorrow off?"

Heather blinked. Why did he keep changing the subject and throwing her off balance? "Yes...that is, I'm not sure. Originally it was agreed that I'd have Saturdays and Sundays off, but I haven't even been here a week yet so..."

"I'll clear it with Jocelyn," he interrupted. "I don't see how she can refuse. After all, you're doing her a favor by staying on until Miss What's-her-name gets here. Will you spend the day with me? We can go sight-seeing if you'd like. You said you'd never been to Boston before."

Heather's head was swimming. It sounded suspiciously like he was asking her for a date.

"Wait a minute," she pleaded as she again lifted her head to look at him. "You're going too fast for me. Why do you want to take me sight-seeing?"

That cocky grin that was so endearing gave him an impish look. "Well, actually that was my second choice, but I was pretty sure you wouldn't spend the day with me at my place no matter how pure my intentions."

She couldn't resist teasing him back. "And just how pure are they?" she asked with feigned suspicion.

His gaze roamed over her face, then settled on her mouth. His impish expression changed to one of longing as he whispered, "Not very," just before his lips took hers and clung.

Somewhere in the back of her mind Heather knew she should push him away, but her arms didn't get the message. They stole around his neck and held him as she returned the kiss and silently begged for it to go on...and on...and on...

Max had to forcibly restrain the passion that had been building in him ever since he'd taken her in his arms to comfort her. Comfort, ha! He hoped she was comforted because he was anything but.

It was all he could do not to hug her closer so he could feel her supple body pressed full-length against his, their legs entwined, and her breasts... Oh, those tantalizing breasts that no amount of clothing could hide. His hands ached to cup their firm softness and stroke the nipples until they hardened.

Her lips under his parted slightly, and he stifled a groan. He'd swear that she didn't know what she was doing to him, and if he gave in to the almost unbearable temptation to explore her sweet mouth with his tongue he'd scare her away. She kissed like the virgin he had no doubt she was, and he was too old and too honorable to deflower her innocence.

Like hell he was! If he didn't get out of here, right now, he was going to teach her a lot of things that only a fiancé should initiate her in.

With his last bit of resolve, he lifted his head and put her away from him. She looked dazed and confused, an expression she wasn't mature enough to fake, and he knew for sure that she was an innocent and he was a cad.

He couldn't resist softening the abruptness of his leave-taking with one last quick kiss, and it was almost his undoing. Tearing his mouth from hers, he stood and looked down at her. "I'll pick you up in the morning at nine o'clock," he said huskily. "We'll start our sight-seeing tour by attending services at Old North Church, where the lantern was hung to alert Paul Revere that the redcoats were coming. It's the oldest church building still standing in Boston. We'll have brunch afterward, so don't eat much breakfast."

He turned and almost ran out of the room and down the stairs, leaving Heather staring after him.

Heather was staring after Max, right enough, and she was also shaken to the soles of her beige pumps. She'd been kissed before, but never with such a devastating mixture of tenderness and passion. At twenty-one she was well aware of her sexuality, but no man had ever stirred it to such a heat as Max just had.

She hadn't fully realized what she'd been missing!

She put her hands to her cheeks and felt the warmth on the outside as well as the inside. This time it wasn't so much embarrassment as it was chagrin. She remembered when she was fifteen and waiting for her first date to pick her up. Daddy had reminded her to be in by midnight, and then he'd stammered slightly when he said, "Th-there's something you should know about boys, Heather. They have strong, uh, sexual urges that are difficult to control. It'll be up to you to set the limits."

He'd been a shy man, and there was a round patch

of color on each of his cheeks as he'd forced himself to go on. "I'm…I'm not saying that's fair, but there's a lot about nature that isn't and that's the way it is with teenage boys. Don't let them do, um, things…to you that feel really good and then expect them to stop. Remember, honey, a good-night kiss at the door is one thing, but necking in the back seat of a car is asking for trouble."

By this time she'd been as embarrassed as he was, and she'd breathed a sigh of relief when the doorbell rang before she had to answer him.

For the past six years she'd followed his advice and set the limits with her dates, but tonight she hadn't even wanted Max to stop. Obviously it was just as well that she wouldn't be here much longer, after all!

She was sitting there trying to deal with her conflicting feelings when the sound of a man self-consciously clearing his throat startled her. Had Max come back?

She raised her head and looked at the doorway, but there was no one there.

"Ah, Mistress Heather, be not frightened," said a voice from the other side of the room. A voice she recognized.

It was the voice of the man in her dream.

She glanced quickly to the right, and saw the tall man in the black-and-white colonial costume standing in the corner beside the large potted fern, which sat on a very old hickory plant stand. She blinked with surprise, but he was looking at her with such compassion that she was reassured rather than frightened.

"I…I thought I'd dreamed you," she said hesitantly.

"I know." His tone was low but clear, with a slight ring to it. Like a bell.

No, not a bell, Heather decided. More of a hollow sound. Like a faint echo.

"Were it in my power I'd let it remain a dream for you," he continued, "but 'tis not possible. You can see me."

"Well, of course I can see you," she said, finally throwing off that peaceful spell he cast, "and I don't think you're supposed to be up here? Who are you, anyway?"

"Ethan Hadleigh," he said, repeating the name he'd given her before.

"Yes, I know your name," she answered impatiently. "What I meant was *who* are you? Do you work for the Sheffields?"

"Nay, I reside here."

She remembered that he'd told her that before, too, but they'd been interrupted before she could question him further. An oversight she intended to correct.

"Mr. Hadleigh, Mrs. Beaufort took me on a tour of this house from the basement to the attic, and not once did she mention that any of the rooms were occupied by someone other than the family. Are you a member of the family?"

He shook his head. "Not recently."

Good heavens, what kind of an answer was that? Was she going to have to pull the information she wanted out of him question by question? "Then why do you stay here?"

"'Tis my land."

That shook her. "You mean you own the land the house is built on?" she asked incredulously.

"Aye. It's been in my family for three hundred years."

Heather gasped. "Three hundred years!"

Obviously this man's strangeness went beyond just the way he looked. Could he have escaped from a mental hospital in the area? That would explain his costume, his odd way of talking and his delusion that he lived in this house.

It was a frightening prospect, but she was puzzled to realize that she wasn't frightened. She couldn't believe that this gentle man was dangerous, but neither could she take any chances. Especially since he was so stealthy that he could come and go without being heard or seen. She was responsible for the baby's safety.

She'd have to report him to the security guards that patrolled the grounds, but if he knew what she was doing, and he was unbalanced, he might become violent.

It would be best to get him off the nursery floor, then turn him over to Franchot. Her employer was a big man whom she was sure could handle the problem.

Ethan Hadleigh still stood quietly, watching her with sad eyes. How could she betray him? On the other hand how could she not? Surely he would go peaceably with the guards and not make it necessary for them to hurt him.

"Mr. Hadleigh," she said carefully, "will you do me a favor and go downstairs with me?"

He shook his head. "Nay, that I cannot do. I reside up here."

Here? On the fourth floor? But that wasn't possible.

"I do not roam the house," he continued, "only this one room."

"But that's not..." Heather's thought processes simply gave out. "I don't understand," she confessed.

A slow smile lifted the corners of Ethan's mouth. "Of course you don't, but even if we went downstairs it would not rid the house of me. Master Franchot cannot see me. Neither can anyone else in the family. You're the first person open and sensitive enough to look upon me in over a hundred years."

Heather felt a chill that traveled up her spine and settled at the back of her neck, like a breeze blowing on tingling nerve ends. Her mouth was suddenly dry and she couldn't swallow as she stared in horrified disbelief at the kindly man who was trying to convince her that she was insane.

Her throat felt like sandpaper, but she forced herself to speak. "Are you telling me that you're a...a *ghost*."

He nodded. "Aye. A spirit. You must not fear me, I would never harm you."

She shook her head, hoping to clear it, but it did no good. "I don't believe you. You're playing tricks on me so I won't call the security officers and have you taken away."

His half smile disappeared. "Mistress Heather," he said, "please get up and go stand in front of the mirror."

He nodded toward the ornate gold framed mirror on the wall over the fireplace.

She stood on shaking legs and walked over to place

herself in front of it. The face that looked back at her was pale and disbelieving.

"What do you see," he asked.

"I see myself, of course," she answered shakily.

"Now what do you see." This time the voice came from directly behind her, and she jumped and turned to see Ethan standing not more than a foot away and in a direct line with her.

"Look in the mirror again and tell me what you see this time," he commanded gently.

She turned slowly, dreading what she knew was going to happen but unable to stop herself.

Again she gazed at her likeness in the glass and, as before, hers was the only reflection. Although she knew Ethan Hadleigh was standing immediately in back of her, the mirror showed her standing alone.

Chapter Four

Heather's first impulse was to deny what she was seeing, to berate Ethan Hadleigh for playing a magician's tricks on her, but deep in her soul she knew that he was exactly what he said he was. A ghost, spirit, wraith, demon—whatever.

No, not a demon. If Ethan was indeed an incarnation from an afterworld, he was a benign one. He radiated warmth and devotion and benevolence. Heather had felt it the first time she'd set foot on this floor, and she was even more aware of it now in his presence.

Finding an apparition in her sitting room was an awesome experience, but she knew she was safe with him.

She turned to face him, and now that she knew his true nature she finally realized what it was about him that had been amiss. He was devoid of color!

She blinked. How could she have missed such a

thing? She'd thought his coarsely woven pants and shirt were black and white, and they probably were, but now she saw that all of him was varying shades of gray, like light and dark shadows.

He looked like a man who had stepped out of an old black-and-white movie. Not flat like a photograph. Ethan was definitely three-dimensional, and he did blend in with his background of dark, rough-hewn furniture and sparse, masculine decoration.

With a sense of wonder she lifted her hand and reached out to feel him, but he stepped back. "We live in different dimensions, Mistress Heather. You would be well advised to get used to seeing and talking to me before you try to touch me."

Heather's face flamed. How could she have been so rude?

"I'm sorry," she apologized. "I had no right..."

He held up his hand. "Your curiosity is natural," he said gently, "but putting your hand on me would be very different from what you expect, and you have enough to absorb right now."

She felt light-headed as she began to get her bearings again. "You're right," she agreed, and walked over to the Windsor armchair where she sank down before her knees gave way.

He continued to stand by the plant, and she said the first thing that came into her mind. "Do you bend?"

"Bend?"

"I mean, can you sit down?" She felt foolish, but how else could she find out? "You've always stood in my presence."

Ethan's smile became a full-fledged musical laugh.

"Of course I can sit," he assured her, and proved it by sitting down on the stool that went with the antique pianoforte. "I can levitate, too. Would you like to see?"

"Oh, my goodness, no," she said hurriedly. "I don't think I'm up to that. Let's save it for another time."

Now that she was coming out of shock, Heather was intrigued with her apartment mate and bursting with questions. It wasn't every day that she was confronted by a ghost!

So far he didn't seem very talkative. He answered her when she spoke, but only occasionally volunteered information. Would it be impolite of her to inquire about his...his history? She wouldn't know unless she tried.

"Do...do you mind if I ask you some questions? Of course, you don't have to answer any that you don't want to."

"I'm honored that you are willing to talk to me. It's been so long since anyone has done that." He grinned. "Obviously one won't talk to somebody one can neither see nor hear. What is it you want to know?"

"Everything," she blurted. "I mean...well...I've never met a ghost before. Do the Sheffields know you're here?"

His expression sobered. "Nay. Oh, the babe does. She's too young to know that I'm not supposed to exist, but she'll lose her innocent acceptance of me before she's old enough to remember. I can sometimes influence the thoughts of those who do not accept the concept of me, but they think it was their own idea.''

Heather's muddled mind cleared. "It was you who 'influenced' Jocelyn to furnish this room in American colonial decor.'' It wasn't a question but a statement.

Again his grin appeared. She was glad that he seemed to be a contented ghost. "Aye,'' he acknowledged smugly, "'tis so. This is my chamber and I wanted the furniture to be of my time. I like it, and it did no harm.''

Heather didn't see it that way. "You frightened her," she said disapprovingly. "She's still puzzled and uneasy.''

Ethan shrugged. "Mistress Beaufort is too self-satisfied and used to having her own way. 'Tis good for her to have her complacency rattled now and then.''

Heather could see that Jocelyn wasn't the only one who was "self-satisfied and used to having her own way,'' so she let the subject drop and picked up another one.

"Would it be impudent of me to ask how old you are?'' she asked hesitantly.

"I gave you the right,'' he reminded her. "The idea of time is different for you than for me, but I had lived for one and forty years when I was killed at the Battle of Lexington in 1775.''

Once again Heather felt a tingle of incredulity. This conversation couldn't be taking place. How could she be talking with a man who'd died more than two hundred years ago!

Drawing a deep breath she forced herself to continue. "You fought in the Revolutionary War?''

He looked thoughtful. "It would appear so. At the time I was just one of the citizens who took up arms and marched with the militia and the minutemen to hold back the British redcoats who were intent on capturing our stores of weapons and gunpowder at Concord. We were not at war, but when we reached the Lexington Common we were fired on." He paused for a moment, then finished. "I was one of those who went down."

His words were so descriptive that in her mind Heather could see the handful of indignant, ill-equipped colonial men exchanging gunfire with a thousand colorfully garbed and professionally trained English soldiers on the flat, grassy green in the center of the small village of Lexington.

She wasn't sure whether condolences were in order when speaking to the deceased himself, but it seemed the thing to do. "I'm so sorry," she said. "Did you have a family?"

He nodded. "Aye. A wife and four children. Also three grandchildren."

"Grandchildren?" Her eyes widened. "But you weren't old enough..."

"I had nearly lived out my allotted time," he informed her. "Life was shorter in those days. I married at eighteen, as did many men, and our eldest child, a daughter, was born nine months later. I was a grand-sire for the first time when I was five and thirty."

A grisly thought occurred to her, and she tensed and clasped her hands together as she spoke it. "Were you, uh, buried on the land around this house?"

He studied her a moment before he answered. "Nay, but we'll speak of that another time. 'Tis late and you are becoming distraught. I'll leave you now. Sleep well."

He disappeared right before her unblinking eyes.

Heather wakened at seven o'clock the following morning feeling marvelously rested, which surprised her. After Ethan Hadleigh's nerve-racking revelation, and then his abrupt disappearance, she'd expected to toss and turn for hours.

She still didn't know whether he'd actually disappeared or if he'd made himself invisible, but he hadn't answered when she'd called to him and she was certain he wouldn't deliberately frighten her. The uncertainty had made her uneasy, though. If he'd disappeared where did he go? And if he was invisible how could she have any privacy with a male ghost in her rooms? Just how male was a ghost?

She obviously hadn't fretted about it because, although she'd locked her bedroom door while she'd undressed, her head had hardly touched the pillow before she was asleep.

Now she tumbled out of bed and wrapped her cotton robe around her as she hurried toward the parlor before seeing to the baby. The room was still empty, and when she called to Ethan he didn't answer.

By eight o'clock Heather had dressed Yvette and was gently rocking her in the sturdy old maple rocker, while coaxing her to take the last of her bottle, when she heard footsteps in the hall and Jocelyn appeared in the open nursery doorway. She was wearing a peach chiffon peignoir with a matching nightgown and slippers, and her dark hair fell in dishabille around her sleep-swollen face.

She fixed Heather with a disapproving glance. "Max told me you wanted today off," she said accusingly.

"I wasn't sure whether or not I'd earned it yet," Heather explained, "but if you don't mind Max has offered to take me sight-seeing since I'll be leaving Boston soon."

Jocelyn frowned and pushed a heavy fall of hair away from her face. "You're entitled to it," she grumbled, obviously displeased about something.

She walked across the room and reached down to take the baby from Heather. "I'll take her down to our rooms so you can dress," she said as she lifted the gurgling child and laid her over her shoulder. "Please meet Max downstairs. We don't allow boyfriends up here."

"Boyfriends?" Heather's voice squeaked with astonishment. This was Max's childhood home, for heaven's sake, and she was quite certain he'd take exception to the term "boyfriend."

Jocelyn walked across the room, then turned at the doorway. "And, Heather, we'll expect you back here by ten o'clock tonight. I have an early appointment at the office tomorrow morning, and I don't want to be wakened in the night by the baby."

She whirled around and strode out the door, leaving Heather sitting there with her mouth open but unable to form words in her jumbled mind.

She puzzled over Jocelyn's behavior as she showered and dressed. Her employer was displeased about something, and the crack about boyfriends seemed to indicate that it was because she was planning to spend the day with Max.

She was well aware that it was against the rules of propriety for a nanny to become romantically involved with a member of the family who employed her, but the Sheffields had made it plain that she was only baby-sitting until more suitable help could be found. In a week she'd be out of there and never see any of them again. Meanwhile, if Max wanted her to spend time with him she wasn't going to say no.

She'd give little Yvette the same quality of care that she'd give a child of her own, but she wasn't going to let this powerful family dictate how she could spend her free time.

Mindful of Jocelyn's demand that she meet Max downstairs Heather was dressed and hurrying down the three flights of steps by ten minutes to nine. As she reached the second floor and started down the last flight she heard voices coming from the first-floor living room. It was a man and a woman, and they were quarreling.

"You needn't glare at me, Maxwell," said the distinctive voice of Daphne Sheffield. "You've always known that young women employed here as household help are not to be flirted with or dated by the men of this family."

"Oh, for God's sake, Ma," Max said angrily, "I don't live here anymore so Heather's not *my* employee. Besides, I'm not going to seduce her, I'm just taking her sight-seeing. She's never been in Boston before."

Anxiously Heather moved a few more steps down to where she could see Max and his mother sitting on the sofa with their backs to the stairway so they didn't see her.

They were talking about her and she didn't want to hear, but before she could speak, Daphne answered. "Don't call me Ma," she snapped, "and don't make the mistake of thinking I'm too old to remember what it is that men your age want from a beautiful young woman. Unfortunately Miss Carmichael is too immature and inexperienced to have learned yet that all she has going for her with you is a great pair of legs and breasts."

"Mother!" Max's tone was a mixture of outrage and amusement. "That's not true, but even if it were, give yourself credit for having raised me with at least a minimum of moral fiber. I promise to bring her back every bit as virginal as she was when I left with her."

"Don't be thickheaded," Mrs. Sheffield grumbled. "That's not all that's bothering me, and you know it."

"Yes, I do." This time Max's tone had changed to disgust. "You're afraid I might get serious and marry her. You're a snob, Mother, and I'm getting more than a little tired of it. When and if I marry it will be a woman of *my* choosing, not yours."

An involuntary gasp from Heather caused them to look over their shoulders and see her standing on the staircase.

Max swore and jumped up. "Heather." He circled the sofa and headed toward her. "We didn't hear you come down."

She was both hurt and angry, and in no mood to placate either of them. "Obviously," she observed.

Max's face turned pink, but it was his mother who

spoke. "You could have made yourself known," she said with only a hint of contrition.

Heather had been raised to respect her elders, and she, along with the rest of the country, had always been in awe of the Sheffields of Boston, but both her respect and her awe had disappeared.

She wasn't going to let this woman treat her like an inferior.

She stared back at Daphne Sheffield and hoped that her glance was as cold as her voice. "There was hardly time. Then, too, if I had I'd never have known what a womanizer your son is."

Her glance shifted to Max. "Great legs and breasts, indeed. And here I thought he was only interested in my fine mind." Her tone was broad with sarcasm.

She turned and started up the steps, but Max caught up with her before she reached the first landing. "Heather, come back here. We have to leave now or we'll be late for the first service at Old North Church."

She looked down at his hand on her arm. "Take your hands off me," she said with all the imperiousness of Lady Macbeth. "If your own mother doesn't trust you not to take my celebrated virginity, then I certainly can't go anywhere with you unchaperoned."

Pulling her arm free, she started back up the stairs with Max right beside her. "Dammit, Heather, I'm sorry you had to hear that...."

She stopped and turned to glare at him. "But you're not sorry that the two of you were talking about me as if I were unworthy of respect."

"That's not true," he roared as they headed up the second flight. "Or maybe it did sound that way to you, but there are some things you have to understand about our family...."

"No, there aren't." She was getting breathless from trying to talk and climb at the same time. "I don't need to know a thing about your family except how your sister wants her baby cared for. I'll be leaving just as soon as the *suitable* nanny can move in, and until then I don't even want to see you again."

They'd reached the third-floor landing, and Heather stopped and turned to him before he could answer. "This is as far as you can go. Mrs. Beaufort told me this morning that I wasn't to bring you up to the fourth floor because *boyfriends* aren't allowed up here."

Max groaned and grabbed her by both arms before she could get away. "My God, you really have had a hell of a morning, haven't you."

He tried to pull her gently to him, but again she twisted out of his grasp and ran up the stairs.

Max was right behind her as she reached the fourth floor and turned toward the parlor. The first thing she saw as she marched through the archway was Ethan standing by the maple secretary, and he was grinning. His amused expression told her that he knew what had taken place during the past ten minutes, and he thought it was funny.

Men! Even the male ghosts were chauvinists!

She glared in his direction and without thinking demanded, "Where have you been?"

His grin widened, but it was Max who spoke. "What? What do you mean, where have I been? I've been right beside you."

She'd forgotten that Max couldn't see Ethan, and didn't even know about him.

Ethan put his finger to his lips in a shushing gesture, obviously a warning not to mention him. "Oh, I...I meant what...what are you doing here?" she improvised. "I told you I've had orders not to bring you up here. Your sister has the same idiotic idea as your mother that there's something, uh, romantic going on between us."

"Our feelings for each other are none of their business," Max snapped, "and I'll come and go as I damn well please in my own family home. The fourth floor was my apartment after my three older brothers moved out, and you can believe I'm going to have words with Jocelyn about her high-handed dictates—"

"No," Heather interrupted. "I don't want any more trouble with your family. Just go away and leave me alone."

Ethan was beaming as though they were putting on a show just for his benefit, and she wanted to tell him to mind his own business, but remembered just in time to hold her tongue.

"I can't do that, Heather," Max answered her. "We have a date to go sight-seeing today, and I'm going to hold you to it. I apologize for my mother and sister, but you're not going to let them spoil our friendship, are you?"

Heather was torn. She was strongly attracted to this man. He'd called their relationship "friendship," and as long as she remembered to keep it on that plane his relatives had no right to interfere.

She sighed and dropped down on the couch, still

out of breath from racing up the stairs. "I don't know, Max. I'd like to see Boston before I leave, and you're the best guide I could hope to find, but—"

"Well, thanks a lot," he muttered, disgruntled. "Is that all going out with me means to you?"

Heather threw up her hands in disgust. What on earth was the matter with him? He'd just made a point of letting her know they were only friends.

"Yes, it is," she said impatiently. "If I've led you to believe otherwise I'm sorry. I didn't think a couple of light kisses would be mistaken for...for passion."

"Light kisses!" he sputtered, and reached for her. "If those were too tame for you I can do a hell of a lot better."

He pulled her to him, but she put her hands on his chest and pushed. He let her go immediately, but not before she saw Ethan's expression change to one of anger as he moved toward where they sat. He stopped when Max released her, but she was intrigued. How did a ghost fight with a man?

Somehow she had no doubt that Ethan could and would protect her. It was like having her father looking after her again, but she also knew that Max would never do anything she didn't want him to.

"I'm sorry," Max said. "I didn't mean to scare you, but I've been looking forward to being with you today. Please don't back out. As you said, I'm the best guide you'll ever find."

She hesitated a moment longer, but she really did want to see the historic monuments in this three-hundred-and-fifty-year-old city before she left. It might be a once-in-a-lifetime chance since she couldn't be sure she'd ever return.

"Oh, all right," she said uncertainly. "I guess it will be okay since I'll be leaving in a few days. Do we still have time to go to church?"

His face lit with pleasure as he stood. "We can catch the second service, but I'll have to reschedule our brunch reservation. May I use your phone?"

She was delighted with the opportunity to get him out of the parlor for a few minutes so she could talk to Ethan. "Of course. There's one in the bedroom."

Max left, and Heather turned to the ghost. "You can wipe that silly grin off your face," she said crossly.

The grin just widened. "Ah, but you were magnificent the way you stood up to Madam Sheffield and her overly indulged son."

"I didn't see you downstairs," Heather said.

"Nay. I told you, I don't venture below this floor."

"Then how did you know what happened there?"

His grin disappeared. "'Tis not something I can explain to you. I dwell on a different level of existence. You would not understand. 'Twill be easier for you if you do not try."

"But I need to know—"

Max's voice interrupted. "Heather, who are you talking to?"

She turned to see him in the archway looking perplexed.

Again Ethan put his finger to his lips.

She did some quick thinking. "Oh, Max, I didn't hear you coming. Were you able to change your reservations?" She picked up her purse and walked toward him.

"Yes," he said, and glanced at his watch, "but if

we don't hurry we'll be late for the last church service."

She took his arm and, with a quick backward glance at an amused Ethan, walked with Max down the three flights of stairs. Her ruse had worked. Max had forgotten about his unanswered question.

As Max and Heather neared Old North Church, the bells in the tower rang to announce the service. Max looked down at her and smiled. "Did you know that the first peal of bells on this continent sounded right here in 1744?"

She shook her head. "No, I didn't. Were they the same bells that are ringing now?"

He hesitated. "I'm not sure, but I believe they are. I know the church is the oldest one in Boston."

Inside they were ushered to a seat in a boxlike pew with a gate that latched, just in time to join in singing the first hymn. As a fairly regular churchgoer, Heather found it an incredibly moving experience to worship with Max in this ancient sanctuary so steeped in the history of the land.

Afterward, in a dizzying shift from the eighteenth to the twentieth century, Max took her to lunch on the fifty-second floor of the Prudential Center. "I hope you like seafood," he said as they rode up in the express elevator, "because the Top of the Hub has a fine reputation for fresh fish."

He was right about that, but it was only one of the many mouth-watering dishes available on the brunch buffet. "Oh, Max," she said plaintively. "Everything looks delicious. How can I make a choice?"

"Take a little of everything," he suggested.

"If only I could, but if I started with the breakfast dishes, progressed through the luncheon entrées and finished with the desserts, it would take me all day and I'd be sick."

He chuckled. "Then I suggest you choose the foods you like best, and next Sunday I'll bring you back for the rest."

A shadow of sadness and regret dimmed her joy, but she didn't remind Max that she wouldn't be seeing him after today. That by next Sunday she'd be back in Atlanta, frantically looking for another position.

Max had reserved a table by the windows, and the view from that height was panoramic and spectacular. It stretched from the gold-domed State House and gracious town houses of Beacon Hill to the distant mountains of southern New Hampshire, from bustling Boston Harbor to the boats sailing on the Charles River and beyond.

By the time they finished brunch, they were both so full that Max suggested a walking tour of historical sights rather than the Beantown sight-seeing trolley he'd planned on catching.

Heather was enthusiastic. "We both need the exercise," she pointed out, "and we can explore much better on foot. I'm a toucher. I like to feel things."

"I'll remember that," Max said with a wicked wink that made her blush.

He drove the car back to the family home and left it there. Heather had already walked the baby in her pram through the Boston Common across the street and past the almost two-hundred-year-old brick State

House at the end of the block so they didn't tarry there.

They began the tour a few blocks away at Kings Chapel. "This was the first Anglican church in New England," Max told her, "and the burying ground beside it contains the grave of John Winthrop, the first governor of the Massachusetts Bay Colony."

They walked hand in hand past Old City Hall and Ben Franklin's statue to the Old Corner Book Store. "This brick building was once the center of the literary community of Boston," Max said, "where Longfellow, Hawthorne, Emerson and Thoreau hung out and probably read their latest manuscripts to one another."

Then on to the Old South Meeting House, a slender brick building with a tall white spire that was almost dwarfed by surrounding skyscrapers.

"This was built in the early 1700s as a Puritan church," Max informed Heather, "but it became famous as the sight of many town meetings leading up to the Revolution."

Inside they sat in one of the pews facing the beautiful raised pulpit and multipaned curved-top windows. It seemed to her that she could almost hear the indignant voices of enraged citizens as they gathered to protest the tax on tea, or the Boston massacre.

A short time later they were standing in front of the Old State House, the sight of the famous massacre. It was a small, unimpressive-looking, red brick building with white framed glass doors leading out onto a balcony on the second floor, but its history was fabulous.

"The State House was the seat of the colonial government," Max pointed out, "and it was here that the clash between a jeering Boston crowd and the British guard resulted in the deaths of several colonists. Actually, it wasn't a massacre at all, but a street fight. The word 'massacre' was used by speech makers to stir the anger of the people."

He grinned. "Not, I should add, unlike the commentators and reporters of today's television and newspapers. It got results, and the Boston Massacre was one of the events that led up to the Revolutionary War."

Heather sighed. "Whoever said 'the pen is mightier than the sword' knew what he was talking about."

Max put his arm around her waist and hugged her against his side. "That's true, but this was also the site of happier events. For instance, the Declaration of Independence was first read to the people from that balcony."

It was a considerable hike to their next stop, but the tour of Paul Revere's house, the oldest home still standing in Boston, was worth it. Heather was intrigued with the restored slate-gray two-story building, and the priceless antique furnishings and colonial atmosphere that clung to the rooms made her think of Ethan. Indeed, his presence was so strong that she found herself looking for him in the shadows.

By the time they stepped out of the house and onto the busy street, Heather's legs ached and her feet hurt from being on them for so long. Her weariness must have shown because, after taking a long look at her, Max flagged a taxi.

"Fascinating though this has been, I think it's time

we took a break before you drop," he said as he helped her into the cab and gave the driver an address.

She settled thankfully on the seat as the car pulled away from the curb. "Where are we going?"

"Home," he said.

"But you gave the driver the wrong address."

He took her hand and held it. "My home. It's only a few blocks from the family place, and if what Mother said has made you doubt my honor you needn't be afraid. I have a housekeeper who'll protect your virtue."

Heather looked at him. There was no sarcasm in his tone, but there was a hint of pain and she realized that he was serious. She also understood that his mother's taunting words had hurt him deeply.

She squeezed his hand. "Max, I never for a moment doubted your honor."

He raised her hand to his lips and kissed it, sending a thrill all the way up her arm. "Thank you for that," he murmured as the cab stopped in front of a row house not unlike his mother's.

Max's house was early Victorian architecture, but it's furnishings were contemporary, which pleased Heather as she gazed around the comfortable living room.

"Oh, I like this," she said breathlessly.

Walking over to the massive modular curved sofa that stood facing the brick fireplace she sank deep into the thick velour cushions with a long, contented sigh. "This is pure heaven," she murmured, and closed her eyes. "I've never sat on anything so comfortable in my whole life."

"I hoped you'd like it," Max said. "What can I get you to drink?"

"A cola would be nice. One with lots of ice."

She opened her eyes and watched him walk across the room and through a door. The floor plan wasn't much different from the family home, but that was the only resemblance between the two. Max's personality permeated this one, and she suspected that he'd kept firm control of the decorating, from the deep brown carpet and beige walls, through the expensive masculine furniture, to the seascapes on the walls.

Max reappeared carrying a tray and followed by a rather dumpy little woman wearing dark slacks and a rose smock. She had blue eyes, gray-streaked brown hair and a bright smile. Max introduced her as "Opal, my housekeeper."

"I'm pleased to meet you, Miss Carmichael," Opal said as she arranged dishes of nuts and pretzels on the heavy oak coffee table. "How's that precious little Yvette? I hope you'll bring her over sometime when you have her out for a walk."

Heather glanced at Max. Obviously Opal knew that Heather was the new nanny, but Max hadn't told her that Heather was being replaced tomorrow. Not wanting to embarrass the woman she let it pass. "Yvette is a joy, and I'd love to bring her over."

At least she hadn't lied. Nothing would please her more than to be able to push Yvette in her pram over here to have coffee and a chat with this nice lady every so often.

Opal left, and Max handed Heather her cola, then

sat down beside her. "Turn and put your feet up here," he said, patting his thighs.

She felt more than a little awkward, but shifted obediently and put her feet in his lap.

"No wonder you're tired," he scolded. "You've been walking all over Boston in those high heels. You should have worn walking shoes."

He slipped off her pumps and took her feet in his hands. She'd never thought of feet as an intimate part of the body, but when his hands moved firmly over hers it sent messages she had no business receiving. Her muscles tightened and she started to pull away.

"Don't resist, honey," he said softly. "Let me massage them. I won't take liberties, I just want to work out the muscle spasms so you can enjoy dinner."

Heather relaxed. It sounded innocent enough, and oh, his touch did such delightful things to her.

She curled against the thickly padded back of the sofa and closed her eyes again. "You're a nice man, Max." Her tone was dreamy. "I'm sorry your mother misunderstands and objects to our friendship."

He continued to rub her insteps with his thumbs. "Let's get one thing straight right now, sweetheart," he said quietly. "She didn't misunderstand my desire, just my intent. I want very much to make love to you, but she's wrong in thinking that I'd take advantage of your youth and innocence to seduce you."

Chapter Five

Max's words sent a wave of heat coursing through Heather, and only a fraction of it was shyness.

He wanted to make love with her! It was a subject she'd skirted in her mind, but never allowed to develop into a full-scale picture. Now she couldn't stop it, and the image of them entwined in each other's arms right there on the sofa left her unable to speak.

He looked at her, and his crooked little smile was almost as endearing as the hunger in his eyes. "I've embarrassed you," he said contritely. "I'm sorry, I didn't mean to. I just want you to know that I spend time with you because I'm very fond of you, and it's a pleasure to be near you. Not because I'm hoping to get you in the sack."

She pushed a lock of hair back from her face, but couldn't bring herself to meet his gaze. "Max," she said, then swallowed and moistened her lips. "I...I guess it's pretty obvious that I haven't been around much. I mean, my mother died before I was in my teens, and after that there was just my dad and I.''

She took a deep breath and continued. ''Daddy was a prize-winning poet and taught literature at the community college in Macon. He was the stereotypical absentminded professor in the ivy tower, and left all the child-raising to Mother. When she died we just sort of bumbled along, taking care of each other.''

Heather smiled as she thought of her tall, slender, sandy-haired father with his thick dark-rimmed glasses and perpetually rumpled clothes.

''He was constantly composing poetry in his mind, which didn't leave much room for anything else, so I had to be the alert one. He was preoccupied, forgetful and klutzy, but he loved me and I adored him.''

Max had stopped massaging her feet, but continued to warm them in his hands. ''Were you lonely?''

''I may have been.'' She paused to consider. ''Yes, I guess I was. I had a lot of acquaintances, but no close friends. After cooking and cleaning, as well as studying, there wasn't time for much socializing. I dated sometimes, but Dad was very strict about that.''

She chuckled as she reminisced. ''When I, um, blossomed into womanhood,'' she said delicately, ''instead of just explaining the menses, he sat me down and gave me an abridged college course in sex education complete with pictures, graphs and the proper medical terms for body parts and functions. You see, he was painfully shy, and that was the only way he could talk about such a personal subject.''

''Didn't he allow you to go out with boys?'' Max asked.

''Oh, yes,'' she answered quickly. ''He wanted me

to be a normal teenager, but I was only allowed to date on weekends and then I had to be in by midnight, even when I was in college. I could have rebelled, but to tell the truth, none of the guys I knew were important enough to me to bother."

"What happened to your dad, Heather?"

The compassion in Max's tone brought a lump to her throat, but she took a deep breath and began. "He had this old clunker of a car that should have been junked, but he was comfortable with it and kept having it repaired instead of replaced."

As always when she spoke of her father's death her voice quavered. "One night he'd been to a poetry reading at a coffee house on the outskirts of town, and on the way home the car stalled on the highway. He...he apparently couldn't get it going again and started walking down the road to get help."

She felt a sob building and tried to stifle it. "He was...he was hit from behind by one of those big, older-model sedans, and his...his head was th-th-thrown against the w-w-windshield..."

The sob ripped through her, and then she was in Max's arms with her face buried in his wide, comforting shoulder.

"Aw, sweetheart, I'm sorry," Max murmured as he rubbed his cheek in her hair. "I shouldn't have asked you to talk about it. I didn't realize your pain was still so raw. Go ahead and cry. Get it all out."

She put her arms around his waist and clung to him, and to the tenderness he was offering. "I'm all right," she assured him when she got the sobs under control. "It's been over a year now. I shouldn't be such a baby." Without thinking, she snuggled into the warmth of his embrace.

His hands roamed lightly over her back. "You're not a baby, you're a loving daughter who misses her father. I hope that when I'm gone my children will have such fond memories of me."

Heather put her hand on his chest and felt his heart beating steadily. "When the time comes, your children will be as shattered as I am over my father."

She could feel his nipple under her palm, and circled it with her finger. His heartbeat speeded up, and she belatedly realized what she was doing and snatched her hand away. He picked it up and put it back where it had been, then held it there.

She didn't attempt to pull away again, but she did raise her head to look at him. "Why are we worrying about your children when you don't even have any?" she asked reasonably.

She'd expected to see that teasing grin of his, but his expression remained serious. "I'm not sure," he said huskily. "The subject just seems to come naturally to mind when I'm with you." He brought her hand up to his lips and kissed her palm.

Heather felt a fluttering deep in the core of her, and she knew she should run, not walk, out of his house and out of his life. She also knew she didn't have the strength to do it as he moved her palm to his cheek and caught her gaze with his own.

Passion blazed in his eyes before he lowered his head and captured her mouth with his.

There was nothing tentative or brotherly about his kiss. His mouth was open, and he gently tugged on her lower lip with his teeth. She'd never been kissed in such a way before, and when she gasped he plunged his tongue into the entrance she'd given him and explored the soft, damp interior.

It was the oddest sensation. Instinctively her tongue dueled with his, then embraced it in a smoldering sensual dance.

She gave as well as received, and when Max's hand cupped her breast, she melted against him and moved her own hand up to caress the side and back of his neck.

It seemed so right to be in his arms, pleasuring him as he was pleasuring her, that it was an emotional wrench when he loosened his hold on her and straightened.

"Much as I'd like to continue this," he said shakily, "I think we'd be better advised to go to dinner."

She blinked. "But—"

He put his finger to her lips where, just seconds before, his mouth had been doing such exciting things to her. "Trust me, sweetheart, it's time to put a stop to this while we still can." He released her and stood. "I have reservations at the Union Oyster House, the oldest restaurant in Boston. It's not far from Faneuil Hall and has an oyster bar that's famous."

After a day of walking through historic Boston, Heather felt steeped in eighteenth-century atmosphere, and the old brick restaurant with sawdust on the floor and high-backed booths added to the mystique. Again she thought of Ethan, and wondered if he'd ever eaten here.

A shiver ran down her spine. She'd never believed in ghosts, and intellectually she had trouble coming to terms with the fact of Ethan's existence. When she was with him he was so real that she forgot he was a spirit, but when he wasn't with her she was never sure that she hadn't dreamed him.

And Ethan wasn't the only male who kept her in a state of turmoil. Max was doing an equally good job of confusing her. She'd gone from being furious with him this morning to making out with him on the couch just a few hours later.

If she didn't stick to her resolve not to see him after tonight, she was going to fall in love with him, and that would be a disaster. She could only barely cope with the loss of her father; if she fell in love with Max and then lost him, too, as she surely would, she'd never recover.

During dinner she found it difficult to pretend to be happy and lighthearted. Every time she looked at Max she was reminded that this would be their last time together. She'd probably see him again before she left, but she'd keep things on a formal basis.

Under no circumstances would she go out with him again.

When they'd finished eating, he put his warm hand over hers on the table. "What would you like to do now?" he asked. "It's too late for more sight-seeing, but we could go someplace and dance if your feet are up to it."

Heather felt a stab of regret as she looked at her watch. "I'd love to, but I can't. I have to be home and back on duty by ten."

Max frowned. "Who says?"

"Mrs. Beaufort. She doesn't want to be wakened in the night by the baby."

"Wakened, hell," he snapped. "She never goes to bed before midnight. She's just afraid you'll spend the night..."

He stopped and looked perturbed.

Heather finished for him. "She's afraid I'll spend the night with you. Yes, that was rather transparent," she said. "I'm beginning to wonder if you're in the habit of seducing the hired help, after all. Both she and your mother seem to think my only purpose in coming here was to pluck you from the family tree and ingratiate myself into your precious family."

The hurt and outrage she'd felt earlier had returned full force, and Heather pushed back her chair and stood. "I'd like to leave now if you don't mind."

"I do mind," Max said as he also stood. "And whatever happened to all that confidence you had in my honor?"

He threw some bills on the table, and taking her arm he escorted her out of the restaurant.

Neither of them spoke on the short ride in the limousine to the family home. The silence was strained, and Heather was miserable. Why had she lashed out at him? It was his mother and sister she was mad at. She really did trust him to be a gentleman at all times.

At the Beacon Street address Max dismissed Nick and walked with her to the house. She couldn't protest because she knew he had to get his car, which was parked in the back.

He unlocked the door and ushered her inside. The lights were on, but there was nobody around. Heather wasn't sure what to do now, so she turned toward him and self-consciously put out her hand. "Goodbye, Max." Her tone was crisp and formal. "Thank you for a lovely day. It's been quite an...experience meeting you and your family, and I shall always treasure the memory."

He took her hand and held it. "Oh, it's been an experience, all right," he said grimly, "but don't count on seeing me only in your memories from now on. I intend to be here tomorrow when the new nanny makes her appearance."

"Oh, no, Max," Heather said, alarm and dismay mingled in her voice. "I don't want any more scenes."

"Just planning to hang your head and slink away, are you?" he asked derisively. "Sorry, darlin', but that's not the way we do it around here. You've been thrust into the middle of a Sheffield family brouhaha whether you like it or not."

He pulled her close by the hand he was holding and put his arms around her. "Now kiss me goodnight," he murmured softly, "and let's make some new memories."

She had no thought of denying him as her arms twined around his neck and she raised her face to his. "So sweet," he whispered as he brushed her mouth with his. "Do you know that you haunt my dreams?"

"Oh, I hope so," she whispered back just before their lips met and clung.

Heather woke the next morning with a feeling of dread. Would Max really come over and make a scene. She didn't doubt that he was capable of it, but she hoped that he'd calmed down after a night's sleep and decide it wasn't worth the bother.

Somehow she didn't believe that for a minute.

She was too uncomfortable and embarrassed to face Mrs. Sheffield and the Beauforts at breakfast after the unpleasantness yesterday, so she called the kitchen on the intercom and asked Inga to send up a pot of coffee along with the baby's bottles.

Miss Zimmerman, the new nanny, was scheduled to be interviewed at Jocelyn's office at ten o'clock. Afterward, if everything went well, she'd be brought to the house to meet her small charge, but for the first time since Heather had been with the Beauforts, Yvette was cranky. Jocelyn wouldn't be pleased.

The child's temperature was normal, there was no sign of a rash and her appetite was good. She'd taken all of her bottle. Heather was puzzled. It could be discomfort from teething, but there was no redness or swelling of her gums.

Ordinarily she'd wait a few hours to see if more symptoms appeared or, as was more likely, if Yvette finally stopped fussing and went to sleep, but this baby was a Sheffield-Beaufort heir. Heather was already in trouble with the family. She wasn't going to make a decision about the child's health without consulting the matriarch.

She'd just stepped to the phone when she heard the rattle of the lumbering old elevator approaching the fourth floor. Oh, dear, now what?

She looked at her watch. It was only ten o'clock. Surely they weren't bringing Miss Zimmerman over this early.

Heather carried the fretful child to the elevator just as the door opened and Daphne Sheffield stepped out. Oh, dear, she'd hoped to avoid a face-to-face confrontation just yet. Still, it had to be done, and now was as good a time as any.

"Mrs. Sheffield, I was just picking up the phone to ring you."

Daphne's eyebrows raised. "Oh. Is something wrong?"

Yvette whimpered, and Heather rubbed her back. "I'm not sure. Yvette woke up cross and restless this morning, but I can't find any reason for it."

Daphne frowned and held out her arms. "Give her to me."

She took the baby who let out a howl and stiffened. "Well, now," Daphne said as she settled the squalling child over her shoulder. "What's the matter with Grandma's little girl?"

She patted the baby and looked at Heather. "Have you called Dr. Quincy?"

Heather shook her head. "No, I wanted to talk to you first. She has no visible symptoms to report to a doctor. Her temperature's normal, she doesn't pull her legs up as she would if she had a stomachache and there are no marks or rashes on her that would indicate a problem. I really don't know what to tell him except that she's fussy."

"Well, all babies get that way at times," Daphne said, surprising Heather with her calmness. "Let's go into the parlor where we can talk."

She led the way into the sitting room and sat down on the sofa. Heather was startled to see Ethan sitting on the pianoforte stool. He hadn't been around earlier. She still couldn't get used to having him appear and disappear out of thin air, and almost spoke to him before she remembered and stopped herself.

How was it possible that she could see him, and Mrs. Sheffield couldn't? He was as plainly visible as any man would be who came into the room. But Ethan wasn't just any man, even though he did have a smile of welcome on his face and a twinkle in his eye.

"Good morning, Mistress Heather," he said, and made her jump with shock. Surely he wouldn't speak to her with another person around. "You're looking most seemly on this beautiful day."

Her eyes widened and she glanced at Mrs. Sheffield to see how she was taking it.

Daphne wasn't reacting at all, but continued to quiet the baby.

Ethan chuckled. "Don't look so alarmed. Madam Sheffield can't hear me."

Of course. That made sense. If she couldn't see him she couldn't hear him, either. He didn't exist for her.

Heather wanted to scold him for teasing her, but couldn't chance being accused of talking to herself again. Instead she stuck her tongue out at him, and he slapped his knee and roared with laughter.

Dammit, it was bad enough to live with a ghost, but to be stuck with one who had an offbeat sense of humor was downright annoying!

It wasn't until she'd relaxed and turned her attention back to Yvette and her grandmother that an eerie omission occurred to Heather. When Ethan slapped his knee there had been no sound of contact between his palm and his leg!

In her efforts to quiet Yvette, Daphne turned the child around to sit on her lap, thus giving Yvette a full view of the room. The baby's eyes were immediately drawn to Ethan and she stopped crying. He grinned and waved his fingers at her and she flailed her chubby arms and laughed.

He'd been right. The little one did see him! She not only saw him, but they played together. While Daphne settled back with a self-satisfied air and explained to Heather that it just took experience to know how to quiet a fussy baby, Ethan made faces and pantomimed, sending Yvette into gales of merriment.

"I suggest we wait awhile and see if she's still cranky later on," Daphne concluded. "If she is, we'll get in touch with the doctor then."

Daphne smiled down at the little girl in her lap, then turned her attention back to Heather. "I came up here to apologize for upsetting you yesterday. It was rude of me to vent my displeasure with my son in a place where we could so easily be overheard."

Heather winced. Mrs. Sheffield wasn't apologizing for being displeased, only for being caught at it. Still, she had said she was sorry. Heather decided it was probably the only expression of regret she was going to get; she might as well be gracious.

"I'm sorry you didn't want Max to take me sightseeing," she said, being equally blunt. "He's an excellent tour guide, and I enjoyed the day very much."

"I'm glad you did." The admission surprised Heather. "It would have been a shame to leave Boston without visiting our national shrines, and I feel that, since you heard my comments out of context, I owe you an explanation."

Heather felt she did, too, and she wasn't going to let her off the hook by denying it.

"From the time our eldest son started noticing

girls, my husband and I ruled that the boys were not to socialize with any of the young women who were employed here at the house,'' Daphne explained. ''Maxwell says I'm a snob, and maybe I am, but those things can get messy and cause a lot of gossip and unpleasantness.''

''Mrs. Sheffield,'' Heather exclaimed angrily. ''I have not been trying to seduce Max—''

''I'm sure you haven't,'' Daphne said, ''but neither did you resist when he made advances to you.''

''He didn't—''

''Obviously he did,'' she snapped, ''and you were as susceptible as all the other women who've come in contact with him. The Sheffield men are spoiled and used to having their own way, and I've rarely seen a girl who could resist them. To the best of my knowledge, Titus, Garrick and Lawrence are faithful to their wives now that they're married, and Maxwell will be, too, if he ever gets around to making that commitment, but in the meantime you're no match for him.''

Heather was outraged. ''How can you talk that way about your own sons?''

''Because I know them,'' she said testily. ''They're rich, handsome and they radiate charm. They have experienced, sophisticated women falling all over them. Good heavens, child, don't you read the gossip columns? Maxwell is one of the most eligible bachelors in the country. Hardly a day goes by that he isn't mentioned in one. They're always trashy innuendos with no substance, of course, but still he wouldn't be written about if he weren't seen around town with so many beautiful women.''

Heather had to admit that Mrs. Sheffield had a point. Max's face and name were splashed all over the tabloids and the gossip and society sections of papers around the country.

It was hard to believe that the public Max and the man she knew were one and the same. Her Max was kind, and loving...

Her Max! When did she start thinking of him as *hers*? Was his mother right? Had she been coming on to him without realizing it?

The baby started to fuss again, and Heather looked toward Ethan. He was no longer entertaining Yvette, but sat quietly on his stool looking thoughtful. She felt exposed and wished he hadn't heard all this, but apparently that was the price one paid for being chummy with a spirit. At least she knew he wouldn't tell anyone else.

Daphne handed the cranky child to Heather and stood. "You probably won't believe this, my dear, but it's you I'm concerned about, not Maxwell. He's obviously attracted to you. He may even convince himself that he's in love, but he won't marry you."

Heather cringed. Even though she knew the woman was speaking the truth, it was painful to hear.

"Maxwell is being groomed for a political career," she continued, "and when he takes a wife she'll be a woman of his own background."

Her tone was kind, even though her words cut. "One thoroughly familiar with bureaucratic protocol and all the infighting that can make or break a candidate. The political arena is no place for a novice. It's a machine that would chew you up and spit you out no matter how good your intentions."

She turned and walked out of the room, leaving Heather to wonder which was the most dangerous, the political machine or Max's mother.

It was Ethan who voiced her thoughts. "Madam Sheffield may be right, you know," he said sadly. "For generations the Sheffield men, including Madam's husband, have played the roué with the ladies during their youth, but they wedded women who would advance their careers. 'Tis not likely that Maxwell will be any different. Are you sure you want to stay here? It would sadden me if you left, but it might be better for you to do so."

Heather leaned back in the chair and patted Yvette's back. She'd stopped fussing and lay quietly against Heather's chest, a soft, warm, little bundle of total dependence and joy.

"In spite of what Mrs. Sheffield may think, I didn't come here hoping to seduce her son into marriage," she answered. "I came to be a nanny, and, yes, I would love to stay on here. I admit that I have...feelings...for Max that I shouldn't have, but I've never considered the possibility of marrying him."

Ethan looked shocked. "Do you mean you would let him have his way with you without the posting of the banns?"

It was difficult for her to keep from smiling. Good grief, he was even more old-fashioned than her father had been, which shouldn't surprise her since he was a couple of hundred years older than Daddy.

On the other hand he had a point. Just what had she meant by that ambiguous statement. Not that it mattered since she'd be leaving at the end of the week, so the problem would never have to be dealt with.

"That's not what I meant," she explained, "but I'll have to admit that I don't know what I'd do if Max put pressure on me to go to bed with him."

She looked up to see Ethan frowning, and she was surprised at how important it was to her to have his approval. "I hope you won't think badly of me, Ethan...Mr. Hadleigh..."

"'Twould please me if you would call me Ethan."

She felt warmed by his unconditional acceptance of her even though she'd disappointed him. "Thank you, Ethan. I don't mean to scandalize you, but you must have noticed that moral values are different now than they were in your day."

"Aye," he agreed. "I know about your modern birth control, and truth to tell I favor the gift you now have to limit the number of children you conceive. Prudence and I had four living babes, but she miscarried several more and almost died during the last one. We slept apart after that."

Heather's heart went out to him. "I'm so sorry," she said.

"Aye, so am I, but the young people nowadays too often misuse this miracle that has been given them. They lie with many partners and miss the special bond between a husband and wife who have known only each other."

Heather smiled at his use of the biblical synonyms, but had to admit they were much softer and more pleasing to the ear.

"I know whereof I speak," he continued. "I was

virgin when I married Prudence, and I remained faithful to her until I died. I wanted no other woman.''

His simple statement of fidelity brought a lump to her throat. It was beautiful, and she wondered if he'd ever thought to tell his wife how he felt about her while they were together.

It was nearly noon before the Beauforts arrived with Miss Zimmerman. Heather heard them on the floor below and knew they'd be coming up to the nursery any minute. She'd finally gotten Yvette to sleep, and hoped they wouldn't waken her.

Heather hurried to her bedroom for a last glance in the mirror. Once more she was wearing the black skirt and white blouse, and wishing for the umpteenth time she had the rest of her clothes that had been left back in Atlanta. She was thoroughly sick of the few outfits she'd brought with her.

She'd done her thick black hair in a French braid, hoping it would make her seem older, more professional, but instead it made her look even more like a schoolgirl.

Turning away from the mirror, she sighed. What difference did it make how she looked? She didn't have to impress Miss Zimmerman, and she'd already failed at that with the Beauforts. She might as well accept defeat and start looking forward to a new position somewhere else.

Footsteps on the last flight of stairs alerted her, and she hurried out into the hallway to greet Jocelyn, Franchot, Miss Zimmerman and Max. Max! Good heavens, he'd really meant it when he'd said he was going to be here today.

He grinned and winked at her, scattering her thoughts, while Franchot introduced her to the new nanny. Apparently she'd met all the qualifications and been hired because he added, "Heather has been our temporary nanny until we could find a permanent one."

She'd expected it, but even so she was crushed.

Miss Zimmerman put out her hand and grasped Heather's in a hearty grip. "How do you do, Miss Carmichael. I understand you also studied at the Peachtree Nanny College in Atlanta."

"Yes, I did," Heather confirmed, and continued to make small talk as she scrutinized the woman. She was big. Not fat, but tall and broad, with a wide mouth filled with prominent teeth, and a modified Roman-type nose. She wore a boxy suit of lightweight tweed and sensible low-heeled oxfords, and her medium-brown hair was worn short and straight.

Although she could never be classified as pretty, she had a pleasant smile and an outgoing personality. If the Beauforts were looking for the stereotypical nanny, they'd be happy with Miss Zimmerman. She was about as different from Heather as it was possible to find.

The woman insisted on seeing her "dear little charge," so Jocelyn and Franchot took her into the nursery, leaving Heather and Max behind. Max took her arm and led her down the hall and into the parlor, then turned and put his arms around her. "You look tired," he said as his lips caressed her face. "Don't you feel well?"

In just a minute she'd pull away and be independent and self-sufficient, but right now she needed his arms around her, his tender concern for her well-being.

She snuggled against him. "I'm all right. It's just that the baby's been cranky this morning, and I had a hard time settling her down. Now they'll probably wake her up again..."

As if on cue, Yvette let out a howl of protest. Heather tried to pull away from Max to go to her, but his hold on her tightened. "Let Jocelyn and Miss Zimmerman quiet her down. After all, she's not your responsibility anymore."

Heather sank back against him. "They've hired her?"

He rubbed the back of her neck. "I'm afraid so. I argued for you with Jocelyn, but eventually had to give in. After all, Yvette is her child, not mine. The contract hasn't been signed yet, but they're just waiting to make sure she and the baby are compatible. That won't be a problem since Yvette gets along with everybody."

"Not today she doesn't," Heather said, and had to raise her voice to be heard over the child's wailing. "She's been like this all morning."

The sound was coming closer, and Max and Heather stepped apart just before Jocelyn and Franchot appeared in the archway, followed by Miss Zimmerman carrying the screaming baby.

They were all trying to quiet Yvette, and Heather noticed Ethan standing in the corner grinning like a Cheshire cat. No wonder he didn't go wherever it was others went when they died. He was having too much fun observing the Sheffield family comedy of errors!

She felt not unlike Alice in Wonderland, and wondered if Lewis Carroll's ghost would be interested in writing about the chaotic wonderland Heather Carmichael had fallen into. He wouldn't even have to make it up!

Jocelyn was apologizing to Miss Zimmerman, who was walking the floor with the baby. "I'm so sorry. Mother said she was fussy this morning, but I've never known her to be this cross. Usually she's so good-natured."

Miss Zimmerman looked skeptical, and Heather spoke up. "Would you like me to take her? She's more used to me."

Miss Zimmerman handed her over with a look of relief, and Heather sat down with the child in her lap. Yvette cried for a minute, then sniffled, and finally lay back against Heather's chest and smiled.

The other adults looked amazed, but Heather could see what was quieting her. Ethan was directly in front of them, turning somersaults in the air without ever touching the floor!

He was manipulating the child so that she would smile and laugh, and the others would think she preferred Heather to the new nanny.

Jocelyn and Franchot looked troubled, and Max looked relieved, until Ethan stopped tumbling in the air and Yvette started to cry again. Ethan stationed himself over in front of the secretary and made no further effort to entertain her, which puzzled Heather.

Jocelyn took her daughter from Heather and she and Franchot went into the nursery to examine the child and see if they could find a reason for her behavior. Miss Zimmerman stayed sitting on the couch, and Max walked over to look out the window.

He had his back to the room when Ethan picked up a cut-crystal vase of spring flowers and walked directly in front of the woman with them. Miss Zimmerman's face blanched as she looked, then did a quick double take.

At first Heather couldn't figure out what was wrong. The nanny couldn't see the ghost, but then Heather realized that Miss Zimmerman could see the vase of flowers. It must have looked to her as if the vase were moving through the air by itself!

Ethan walked slowly around the room, with Miss Zimmerman's shocked gaze following his every move, then returned to the secretary and put the flowers down again.

Heather was almost as shocked as the nanny, but for a different reason. This clown who called himself a spirit was going too far. His little joke wasn't funny.

She frowned her displeasure at Ethan just as Miss Zimmerman turned to her, her eyes wide with disbelief. "Did...did you see that?" Her voice was little more than a whisper.

"See what?" Heather asked, not to mislead her but because she hadn't expected the question and wasn't sure just how much the woman had seen.

Miss Zimmerman blinked. "Oh, nothing, I just thought..."

Her voice trailed off and Heather followed her gaze across the room to where Ethan was lifting a large picture off the wall. He held it in front of himself and walked slowly toward the hapless nanny who sat rooted to the sofa, her eyes bulging and her mouth open in a silent scream.

"Ethan, dammit...!" Heather shouted, but was

drowned out by a loud crash as the ghost let loose of the heavy picture and it dropped to the floor.

Miss Zimmerman's silent scream became an ear-splitting shriek as she bolted from the chair and tore out of the room and down the stairs, with Heather and a startled Max right behind her.

Chapter Six

Max and Heather caught up with Miss Zimmerman in the middle of the last flight of stairs, just before she reached the ground floor. Jocelyn and Franchot, jolted by the scream, were right behind them with the howling baby, and Daphne Sheffield stood in the middle of the living room below, looking astounded.

Max caught the panic-stricken nanny by the arm, but she continued down the steps where he finally managed to stop her. "Miss Zimmerman, for God's sake, what's wrong? What was that crash? Are you hurt?" He held her by the arms with both hands.

"The...the...the flowers." She gasped. "The...the...picture..." She kept blinking her eyes and drawing deep breaths, and Max could feel her shaking violently.

Good Lord, what had upset her so? He'd been standing at the window, watching a group of Boy Scouts practicing an Indian dance on the Common across the street, and everything had been quiet, until suddenly there was a crash and a shriek that would have raised the dead. Something heavy had apparently fallen, but she didn't seem to be injured. She was terrified!

It was pure bedlam with everyone around them shouting to be heard over Yvette's bawling. Max couldn't even think, let alone calm this crazy woman who was bucking and twisting in his grasp and clawing at his hands, trying to loosen his hold so she could get away. She was strong, and it was all he could do to hang on to her.

"Quiet!" he roared, and was immediately obeyed by all but Yvette, who just cried louder. "Miss Zimmerman, please calm down and stop fighting me," he said in a lowered voice. "What's the matter with you? If you were injured during that crash we'll get you medical attention, but I have to know what happened."

She focused her eyes on him and took a deep breath in an obvious effort to bring herself under control. "I'm not hurt." She gulped. "I just want to get out of here. If you're playing tricks on me you've gone too far. I wouldn't work here if it were the last job in the world." Her tone was tinged with hysteria.

Max couldn't make sense out of anything she said. "What tricks? What on earth are you talking about? Look, let me get you a drink, or a cup of coffee, if you prefer, and we'll sit down and discuss this rationally—"

"No!" It sounded more like a wail than a word. "I'm not going to spend another minute in this house. Now let me go!"

He'd loosened his grip, and this time when she pulled against him she managed to get away and headed for the front door. It was locked and she threw herself against it.

Max started toward her, but Heather was there before him. She put her hand on the woman's shoulder and said quietly, "Miss Zimmerman, there's no need for you to be so frightened. No one's going to hurt you. Just promise that you'll stay on the front porch and talk to us, and I'll let you out. We can't have you running into the street and getting yourself killed."

Max watched as Heather's calm demeanor seemed to help quiet Miss Zimmerman. She nodded. "All right, but I'd be a hell of a lot safer in the street than I am in here."

What did she mean by that? Max wondered as he moved closer so he could grab the woman if she ran. Heather slid back the bolt and opened the door. Miss Zimmerman almost tripped in her haste to get out, but once on the marble stoop, she stopped and turned to face Heather and Max.

"I'm going back to the airport and catch the first plane out of here," she said jerkily.

Max nodded. "If that's what you want I'll have the limousine brought around." He motioned to Franchot, who went to tell Nick. "I'm sorry that something has frightened you so badly, but if you won't tell me what it was I can't do anything about it."

Miss Zimmerman looked from Max to Heather, and her expression changed from fear to anger. Slowly she lifted her arm and pointed at Heather.

"*She* did it." The nanny's tone was icy with accusation. "I don't know how, but she did it. That woman is a witch!"

Heather gasped and turned white, and a wave of rage coursed through Max. No one was going to call Heather names as long as he was around. He reached out and drew her into his arms, and his heart speeded up as it always did when she snuggled against him.

"That will be enough," he said over her head, and his tone had the sting of command. "We've tried to be reasonable with you, but you're obviously unbalanced. The chauffeur will buy you a return ticket and put you on the plane. After that, I'd advise you never to try to contact us again."

"Don't worry." Miss Zimmerman sneered. "Nothing could get me to come back here."

Just then the limo drove up to the curb. Nick got out and opened the back door as Franchot and Jocelyn came from the house to take charge of seeing their latest nanny candidate off. Max led Heather back inside.

"What on earth was that all about?" asked his indignant mother.

"I haven't the faintest idea," he answered as he looked down at Heather still cradled in his arms. "Jocelyn and Franchot had taken the baby to the nursery, and Heather and I were in the parlor with Miss Zimmerman, when all of a sudden she started to scream and tore out of the room. Do you know what scared her, honey?"

Heather wished he hadn't asked her that. She hated to lie, but if she told the truth they'd be sure she and Miss Zimmerman were both crazy. Just wait till she got her hands on Ethan!

She straightened and reluctantly pulled out of Max's comforting embrace. He seemed equally reluctant to let her go. "That heavy oil portrait by John Copley fell off the wall just before she screamed. Maybe the noise frightened her."

Heather knew she had to get back upstairs before anyone else and move the picture closer to the wall. In all the confusion, Max apparently hadn't noticed it as they ran out of the room in pursuit of the panic-stricken nanny. She'd never be able to explain its being in the middle of the floor where Ethan had carried it before he let it drop.

Franchot and Jocelyn came back into the house, and Jocelyn handed her crying daughter to Heather. "Here," she said, "take her up to the nursery and see if you can quiet her down. I need a drink."

Heather took Yvette and headed for the stairs while Jocelyn made for the bar, complaining loudly about the incompetent help that agencies tried to pawn off on unsuspecting employers.

Heather bounced Yvette in her arms as she climbed the stairs, and by the time they reached the fourth floor the baby had stopped crying and was enjoying herself.

Heather headed immediately for the parlor to find that the picture, which appeared to be undamaged, had been returned to its place on the wall, and Ethan was sitting on the Windsor chair, looking uncertain.

She wasted no time lighting into him. "Ethan Hadleigh, shame on you! How could you do such a thing?"

"I only wanted to spook her a little so she wouldn't stay here," he said sheepishly.

"*Spook* her! You nearly scared her to death! The poor woman couldn't get out of the house fast enough...." She stopped talking because he wasn't paying any attention. Instead he was motioning with his hand and pointing at Yvette to make her laugh.

"Ethan, you're not listening to me," she said crossly.

"Nay, I'm not." He poked at the child without actually touching her, and she squealed with delight. "You scold like a fishwife, and since I'm no longer bound by earthly rules, I don't have to be polite and listen to you."

He looked at her with a teasing grin and, unable to resist his silent appeal, she dissolved in laughter.

"You really are impossible, do you know that?" she chided lightly when she'd calmed down to a giggle.

"Of course," he said with a smile. "Ghosts are always impossible. They don't reflect in a mirror, and if they are seen at all in a photograph it's as a shadow or blot, so how could they be possible?"

"Now don't start that with me," she warned.

He looked surprised. "Start what?"

She shrugged. "It's just modern slang for 'don't tease me,' but you must promise not to ever scare anyone again the way you did Miss Zimmerman. People don't understand levitation, and it frightens them.

"I wasn't levitating," he said innocently. "I was just carrying the vase and picture across the room."

She fixed him with a no-nonsense glare. "Yes, but she couldn't see you, as you very well know. It looked to her like those objects were floating through space without support, which is exactly what you wanted her to think. Now promise me that you won't do that again."

He smiled, blew her a kiss and disappeared right before her eyes without agreeing to anything.

An hour later Heather had given the baby her bottle and was still sitting in the nursery with the sleeping child in her arms. She loved the peaceful rhythm of rocking gently back and forth with the warm, relaxed little body snuggled against her, smelling of baby powder and milk.

Apparently, thanks to Ethan, she had another reprieve before she had to leave the Sheffields, but she wasn't sure that was good. Every day that she stayed here she became more attached to Yvette, and to Yvette's Uncle Max. It would have torn her apart if she'd had to leave them at the end of the week as she'd expected. Another week or two and the pain would be unbearable.

She looked down at the sleeping baby and smiled as Yvette worked her mouth in a sucking motion even though there was no nipple in it. Her nearly bald head was damp with perspiration, and her closed eyelids were topped with long, thick lashes that lay against delicate pink skin.

Heather was so engrossed in the child that she didn't hear Max until he appeared in the open doorway. She looked up and smiled as she put her finger to her lips. He smiled back and tiptoed across the floor to hunker down beside her, then leaned over and kissed her lingeringly. His mouth was warm, and clinging, and set her blood to racing.

"If I were a painter I'd paint you just like this,"

he whispered. "I've never seen a more beautiful Madonna."

She put her palm to his cheek and massaged it gently with her fingers. "Do you like Madonnas?" she whispered back, meaning the paintings.

"I like you," he answered, and turned his head so he could kiss her palm. "And I like the thought of you nursing my babies."

His confession startled her, and she wasn't altogether flattered. "When I have babies they'll be born into a happy marriage," she said crisply, "and their father will be my husband, a man who loves me."

She hated the way she sounded, so prim and proper, but she couldn't bear it if he was leading up to proposing either a marriage of convenience or a surrogate-mother arrangement just so she would provide him with an heir.

Max frowned and drew away. "If you're accusing me of scattering illegitimate sons and daughters around the country, then I'm sorry that you have such a low opinion of me," he snapped, and stood. "I came to tell you that lunch will be served in a few minutes. Velma's coming to stay with the baby."

He turned and walked out, and she heard his footsteps going doing the stairs.

Heather felt as though she'd been slapped, and worse, she knew she deserved his wrath. Why couldn't she ever remember to think before she popped off? She hadn't meant it the way he thought, but she could see how he'd think she did.

Darn! She'd hurt and insulted him, and that was the last thing she'd ever deliberately do.

The maid came while Heather was tucking Yvette

into her crib, and she hurried down to the dining room, where she found Mrs. Sheffield, the Beauforts and Max already assembled. Franchot and Max stood when she entered, but although she tried to catch Max's attention, he wouldn't look at her. It was Franchot who came to greet her and escort her to the table. She bypassed the seat next to Jocelyn and took the one beside Max.

He nodded briefly to her but said nothing as Inga ladled thick white clam chowder into the soup bowls, then passed silver trays of sandwiches and poured wine.

While the others ate, Heather leaned toward Max and said softly, "Max, I'm sorry. I don't know what got into me, but I truly didn't mean to insult you."

He looked at her then, and she could see the outrage that clouded his eyes. "In that case I'll accept your apology," he said icily, and returned to eating his soup.

Obviously he wasn't inclined to forgive her.

She reached under the table and put her hand over his where it lay on his thigh. "Please," she entreated, "I can't stand to see you hurt."

Again he turned to her, and this time his gaze sought hers questioningly. It roamed over her face, then returned to her expressive blue eyes before it softened a little. "I think you mean that," he said hesitantly.

She squeezed his hand. "I do. I feel your pain."

She lowered her gaze, embarrassed. "I...I shouldn't admit that. It puts you in an awkward position...."

He turned his hand over and clutched hers, and his

green eyes seemed brighter than usual. "No, love, it puts me in a very enviable position. No one's ever said that to me before." There was a catch in his voice. "Not even my mother."

He raised their joined hands to his mouth and kissed hers just as Franchot's amused voice broke the spell. "Max, old man, if you could divert your attention to the rest of us for a moment we have things to discuss."

Max looked chagrined and dropped their hands back in his lap, but refused to release hers. Heather noticed that his mother and sister both frowned disapprovingly, and figured she was in trouble again.

Franchot seemed to be the only one enjoying the situation, but when he spoke once more, his tone was serious. "Heather, my dear, we're all so sorry you were put through that dreadful scene earlier. I can't imagine what could have gotten into Miss Zimmerman. Her references were excellent, and she'd seemed so sensible and capable during the interview."

He cleared his throat and took a swallow of coffee. "I've been on the phone to the Peachtree Nanny College, and they could hardly believe what I was telling them. I asked them to send us another nanny, but they seemed a little reluctant and said they'd get back to me after they've had a chance to question her themselves."

Heather sincerely hoped this incident wasn't going to damage Miss Zimmerman's reputation and make it hard for her to find another position. She was going to have to make Ethan understand the extent of the damage he'd done and see to it that he never attempted anything like that again.

"Mr. Beaufort, I'm sure Miss Zimmerman is an excellent nanny," Heather said. "Maybe she just needs a little rest."

Franchot waved his hand in a dismissive gesture. "Well, that's not our problem. Now I'm afraid I'm going to impose on your patience and understanding once more and ask you to stay on a little longer."

Heather had been sure this was coming, and she really did want the position, but they were still only offering temporary employment. She'd be an idiot to court the heartbreak that was sure to come if she stayed.

Before she could make up her mind, Max spoke for her. "That's not good enough, Franchot, and you know it. I've sent her résumé to the two top agencies here in Boston, and they've already gotten back to me with three requests for interviews..."

Heather gasped with surprise. "Max, you didn't tell me that!"

He looked only slightly repentant. "I know, honey, but trained nannies are hard to find. These jobs will wait, and I was hoping Miss Zimmerman wouldn't be acceptable and you could stay on here."

He glared at Jocelyn. "Unfortunately my stubborn sister is being difficult."

Jocelyn glared back at him. "Oh, shut up, Max. This is none of your business."

"Maybe not," he snapped, "but Heather needs a lawyer to protect her interests, and unless she objects I'm going to represent her."

He looked at Heather and she nodded her consent, too dazed to protest.

Max smiled at her, then continued. "All three of

the families offering a position are frantic to find a nanny of Heather's caliber, and they don't care that she's young. Also, the Peachtree Nanny College was less than enthusiastic about sending a third candidate to you. If you don't want to stay home and change diapers yourself, dear sister, you'd better make Heather an offer we'll accept."

It was Franchot who answered. "You make it sound as if we were dissatisfied with Heather, and that's not true. Frankly I think she's doing an outstanding job with the baby, but she is very young and if Jocelyn is uncomfortable with that..."

His voice trailed off and Jocelyn interrupted. "I agree with my husband," she said, speaking to Heather. "You're not only competent, but you care about Yvette." She sighed. "I guess the age thing isn't so important, after all."

She turned to Mrs. Sheffield. "What do you think, Mother?"

Daphne Sheffield crumpled her napkin and put it on the table. "I, too, agree that Miss Carmichael is an excellent nanny, and since she is no longer free to accept a temporary position I'd advise you to sign the agreed-on contract."

She stood and scowled down the table at Max. "Maxwell, I want to see you in my office before you leave." It was a command, not a request.

Half an hour later Max stood in front of his mother's closed office door and wordlessly chided himself for hesitating. Why did a summons from her always make him feel like a little boy about to be chastised?

He was thirty years old and could hold his own

with his older brothers and sister, but although he put on a good show of standing up to her, she intimidated the hell out of him.

Probably because he was the youngest, the baby. She'd been forty-one when he was born, and her other children had ranged in age from six to sixteen. To put it mildly he'd been a surprise. His parents were old enough to be his grandparents, and if they'd ever delighted in small children they'd gotten over it by the time he came along. They'd had no patience with childish mischief, and he'd spent a lot of time being punished for his misdeeds.

Now after four years of college, four years of law school and three years as the junior member of the family law firm, she still treated him like a naughty ten-year-old.

Squaring his shoulders, he knocked on the door, then opened it and went in.

Daphne was sitting behind her desk, looking every inch the elegant matriarch of the Sheffield dynasty. Even as she entered her seventh decade she was a beautiful woman. Her clothes were made for her by the most famous designers in the world, but Max suspected that she'd look regal in burlap.

"You wanted to see me," he reminded her as he took the chair across the desk from her in the book-lined library, which doubled as an office.

"Yes, I did," she replied coolly. "I want to know why it's so important to you that your sister retain Miss Carmichael as nanny. Jocelyn's right; it isn't any of your business."

He shrugged and strove for equal coolness. "She's a sweet kid, and I'm not going to stand by and let you take advantage of her. Since when has the Sheffield family started shafting those who aren't sophisticated enough to know they're being taken?''

Daphne winced. ''Must you be so crude? Or do you do it just to upset me?''

Max felt a wave of guilt. ''I expect that I do, Mother,'' he admitted. ''I'm sorry, but I can't seem to resist a little jab now and then just to see if I can make you take me seriously.''

She sighed and leaned back in her chair. ''I always take you seriously, Maxwell,'' she said, and he realized that she looked and sounded tired. Why hadn't he ever noticed that before?

''Unfortunately,'' she continued, ''you too often act like a schoolboy instead of a grown man, and I can't help but wonder if that's what's happening now with this girl.''

''She's not a girl,'' he protested. ''She's a woman.''

''She's little more than a child,'' Daphne said, ''and you know it. Why else would you be so determined to protect her from your own family? It's not Jocelyn who's taking advantage of her, it's you. You've turned on that charm of yours, and it's easy to see that she's infatuated. Grow up, Maxwell, and take responsibility for your actions.''

He leaped from the chair and slapped the palm of his hand on the desktop. ''Dammit, Ma, I haven't done anything to her!''

Daphne rose with all the majesty at her command, and although she was several inches shorter than he, she seemed to tower over him. ''Maybe nothing, uh, irreversible yet, but you're toying with her emotions.

If Heather Carmichael is going to work here, I want you to leave her alone. I will not have my son seducing a young woman who works in my home!''

Max glared at her through a red haze of rage and pain, then turned and stalked out of the room, slamming the door behind him.

By Friday Heather had neither seen nor heard from Max since he'd negotiated her contract with the Beauforts on Monday, then left to meet his mother in her office as she'd requested. Heather knew that mother and son had quarrelled—everyone in the house knew it—but since it wasn't discussed in front of her, she didn't know what the disagreement had been about.

Now, four days later, she was feeling abandoned and hurt. He'd seemed so anxious for her to stay in Boston, preferably in his mother's house, but once she was signed, sealed and delivered, so to speak, he'd apparently lost interest.

She should have known better than to expect anything else. She'd been a challenge for him, a new diversion, and she'd made the mistake of letting him know how easily he captivated her with his practiced charm. She'd played Cinderella to his prince without remembering that it was all make-believe. That real life princes may dally with the chambermaid, or in her case the nanny, but they married the princess.

Ethan had warned her of that, but she hadn't listened. Mrs. Sheffield had been right; she was way out of her league with a man of Max's fame and fortune.

And thinking of Ethan, she hadn't seen him, either, since Monday when she'd tried to make him promise not to scare the wits out of anyone again and he'd vanished. Oh, God, had she driven him off, too?

A cry from the nursery snapped her out of her reverie. Good heavens, she really was in bad shape if she'd come to the point of mourning the loss of a ghost!

Heather had gotten into the habit of taking Yvette for a walk in the baby carriage in the late morning before the heat became too uncomfortable. Usually she walked in the Common across the street, or up and down Beacon Street, but today she was feeling lonely and in need of someone to talk to.

Max's housekeeper, Opal, came to mind. She'd invited Heather to come over and bring the baby sometime, so why not now? Heather blotted out the disturbing suspicion that she was looking for an excuse to go to Max. After all, it was a workday and he'd be at the office. She'd just drop by, maybe have a glass of iced tea, then leave. He'd never even know she'd been there.

After notifying security, she put Yvette in the buggy and left the house. She still couldn't get used to the idea of being followed everywhere she went with the child.

She'd never seen the security guards. They were as invisible as Ethan was when he wanted to be, but she'd been assured that they were always with her when she had the baby out, and warned that she was never to take Yvette away from the house without notifying them.

The stroll to Max's home was a pleasant one, up winding cobblestone sidewalks and past beautiful old brick row houses, some of them five and six stories high. She rang the bell at the kitchen door and was greeted enthusiastically by Opal.

"Heather! I was afraid you'd forgotten your promise to bring the baby over." She scooped Yvette up in her arms and carried her into the kitchen while Heather pushed the buggy in after her.

"My goodness, how she's grown," the housekeeper observed as she chucked Yvette under her double chins and made her laugh, then motioned toward the table. "Sit down, sit down. What do you want to drink? Mr. Max has everything, so just name it."

Heather asked for a soda, and Opal got it out of the refrigerator with one hand while juggling the baby with the other. She also put homemade cookies on a crystal plate and set it on the table before settling down in the chair across from Heather with the little one in her lap.

"Ah, now, tell me about yourself. With that accent you've got to have been raised in the South."

Heather laughed and admitted that she'd been born and raised in middle Georgia, then at Opal's urging gave a brief sketch of her life. "So now I've been transplanted to Boston," she concluded, "and I love it."

Opal grunted. "Wait until winter when it snows and gets well below zero," she warned. "You might change your mind. Last year we had a blizzard that—"

The chime of the doorbell interrupted, and she frowned. "Now who can that be? I'm not expecting anyone. Excuse me." She stood and hustled out of the room, carrying the baby with her.

Heather heard muffled voices, but didn't pay much attention until the kitchen door opened and Max walked in. He looked disgruntled.

"I went to Mother's house and was told you were over here," he said without even offering a greeting first.

Heather's eyes widened. "How did she know I was here?"

"She didn't, but the security people did," he answered. "They keep in touch by walkie-talkie. Opal says you came to see her."

"Yes, I did," she admitted as she stood, fearing he was going to ask her to leave.

"Why don't you ever come to see me?" he demanded.

Heather blinked. "Well, it's...it's not my place..."

Max groaned. "Oh, no, has Mother been giving you the old nonsense about employer-employee relationships. Dammit, I'll—"

"I don't know what you're talking about," Heather interrupted. "Opal invited me to bring Yvette over sometime, so I did." She sighed with frustration. "What do you want of me, Max? I never know what to expect from you. Half the time you're so warm and...and friendly, and other times you act as if you'd forgotten I existed. I haven't seen or heard from you since Monday so I assumed..."

Her voice trailed off as he moved closer and took her face in his hands. "Friendly, huh," he said huskily as he gazed into her blue eyes. "I lie awake nights, wishing I could show you just how friendly I can be."

He touched her mouth gently with his. "What do

I want of you?'' he said quizzically. ''My lips burn for the taste of yours, and my fingers tingle at the thought of twining with your ebony hair.''

He stroked a black curl back from her creamy temple and eased his hands through the heavy silken strands that fell to her shoulders. They continued down her back until they met, and clasped, at her waist.

''My arms ache to hold you,'' he murmured as he cradled her full-length against him, ''and my palms itch to cup and caress those high, full breasts.''

For a moment she was afraid he wasn't going to act on that last desire, but then, almost as though he'd lost a battle with restraint, his hands slid up her sides and closed gently around her throbbing flesh through the soft pink cotton knit shirt she wore.

Her insides felt like wax being melted in a slow, hot heat, and her heart pounded against his caressing palm. She cuddled against him and held him around the waist as she trailed kisses down the side of his neck before resting her cheek against his shoulder.

He shivered and held her closer. ''Oh, God, Heather.'' His voice was a hoarse whisper. ''No other woman has ever affected me the way you do. When we're apart I can't think straight, and when I'm with you I can't keep my hands off you. If we were together every day I'd take you to bed. I wouldn't be able to help it.''

He lowered his head and nuzzled the beating pulse under her jaw. ''I'm no saint, but I do have scruples that I try to live up to. One of them is not to seduce a sweet, young virgin.''

"Not even if she wants to be seduced?" she murmured huskily, and was surprised by her boldness.

He moved his lips to her ear. "Not even then," he whispered and sucked gently on her lobe, setting tiny fires in her most intimate places. "You're not the type for casual encounters, and marriage isn't something I'm contemplating in the foreseeable future."

Heather didn't know whether he'd done it on purpose or not, but the fires he'd been kindling were effectively doused by his words, leaving her feeling rejected and painfully embarrassed. He was warning her that he wanted her, but he didn't love her and had no intention of making her his wife.

She burned with humiliation. How could she have made such a fool of herself? She'd practically begged him to make love with her, and he'd turned her down! Now she had to find a way to make a dignified exit without letting him know how shattered she was.

Maybe she could use Yvette as an excuse. She could say— Suddenly her sluggish mind clicked back into high gear and was working again. Yvette! Good heavens, where was the baby!

She pushed herself away from Max and looked around. "Where's Yvette," she asked, a note of panic in her tone.

Max reached for her again, but she stepped away. "Opal has the baby," he said. "They're in the living room. Come back here, honey. Yvette's all right, Opal will take good care of her."

The fear drained from Heather, and relief washed over her. "Oh, yes, well, I appreciate Opal looking after her, but she's my responsibility. I should never have let her out of my sight."

PHYLLIS HALLDORSON   131

She hurried toward the door to the front part of the house with Max right behind her. Opal was sitting in the leather recliner, holding the baby in her lap and talking nonsense to her.

She looked up as Heather and Max came in and smiled. "Isn't she just the sweetest little thing you ever saw?" the housekeeper cooed as Yvette reached for her glasses. "No, no, sweetie," she said, and captured the little hand before it made contact. "If you break my glasses I won't be able to see."

Heather walked across the room and took the child from her. "Thank you for keeping her company," she said graciously, "but I really must be going."

Max caught Heather by the arm. "Don't leave. Stay and have lunch with me."

Her arm tingled where his hand touched it, and she breathed a little prayer of thanks that she had such an iron-clad excuse for refusing. She even managed a smile. "Thank you, Max, but I can't. I have to go home and feed the baby."

He frowned. "Tell me what you need, and I'll go to the grocery store and pick it up."

"Oh, no, I couldn't do that," she protested. "Mrs. Beaufort expects me to keep her daughter at home. We only stopped in here to say hello to Opal because we came this way during our regular morning walk."

"Jocelyn won't mind that you've brought Yvette over here," he argued. "After all, I am her uncle. It's not as if she were among strangers."

Heather's only desire was to get out of there, away from this man who had such a powerful emotional hold on her. Apparently he wasn't going to accept a polite no so she'd have to make it stronger.

"Please understand," she said crisply. "I'm a working woman and I'm on duty. My professional reputation depends on how well I follow orders, and since Mrs. Beaufort is the one who's paying me, hers are the orders I'll follow."

Max dropped his hand and stared at her with astonishment as she turned to the housekeeper. "Goodbye, Opal, it was nice chatting with you," she said pleasantly, then walked into the kitchen where she put the baby in the carriage and left.

Chapter Seven

Heather managed to pull herself together as she slowly pushed the pram toward the Sheffield family home. Leaving the buggy in the garage she carried Yvette into the house and was confronted by Daphne as she entered the living room. "Miss Carmichael, did Maxwell find you?" she asked in that imperial tone that indicated her displeasure.

Heather winced inwardly, but managed a wide smile as she answered. "Yes, he did. Actually, Yvette and I were in his kitchen visiting with Opal when he arrived."

Daphne frowned. "I see. Do you go to his home often?"

Heather's smile disappeared, and her stomach muscles clenched with anger. "No, Mrs. Sheffield, I do not," she said coldly. "Surely your security people can tell you that. I've only been there once before and that was when he took me sight-seeing. We stopped there to freshen up before going out to dinner." She turned and started for the staircase. "If you'll excuse me it's time for Yvette's bottle."

After climbing three flights of stairs, her anger had cooled a bit, but Max's mother's implied accusation still rankled. Obviously she was overstepping the bounds of propriety where he was concerned, and making an even bigger fool of herself than she'd thought.

Well, it was her employer's house and, as she'd told Max, they made the rules. From now on she'd abide by them and behave like a proper employee. He'd been honest enough to make it plain that he was only trifling with her. This time she wasn't going to let him sidetrack her.

After changing and feeding the baby, Heather put her down for a nap and wandered disconsolately into her parlor. To her surprise and immense relief Ethan was there, standing in his favorite corner by the fern.

Her mood immediately lightened, and her face broke into a sunny smile as she hurried toward him with her arms outstretched. "Ethan! I was so afraid you were mad at me and would never come back."

Just as she reached him he disappeared, and she was left hugging empty space.

Losing her balance she stumbled, but managed to catch hold of the flower stand and keep from falling.

"Ethan?" she called, off balance emotionally as well as physically.

"I'm over here, child," he said from behind her, and there was sorrow in his tone.

She righted herself and turned to see him standing across the room by the secretary. His expression was heavy with remorse, and if he'd been playing a trick on her it hadn't amused him.

"I...I'm sorry," she said, assuming that in her exuberance she'd managed to offend him. "It's just that I was so glad to see you. I forgot that you don't like to be touched."

He shook his head sadly. "Ah, no, my dear, you misunderstand. I greatly miss the intimacy of the human touch. Would that I could be embraced by you. 'Twould be an experience I'd savor for eternity, but 'tis not possible, and I did not want you to be shocked or frightened."

"I...I don't know what you mean," she said, unable to sort out his words and make sense of them.

"Of course you don't," he said kindly. "There's nothing in your experience to prepare you for me. Come closer and I'll show you."

She was suddenly apprehensive. Again he seemed to read her mind and spoke softly. "'Tis all right. I won't hurt you. I just want you to understand why there can be no touching between us, even though 'twould be my greatest joy."

The warmth that always radiated from Ethan engulfed her, and she lost all fear as she walked forward. When she stood directly in front of him she stopped, and he put out his arm. "Now put your hand on mine."

For a moment she hesitated, then slowly reached out and laid her hand directly on his. Although she could see that they were touching there was nothing beneath her palm but the feeling of a sharp tingle, like a low-voltage electrical shock.

Instinctively she snatched her arm back and

grabbed her hand with the other one as her baffled gaze sought his.

"Try again?" he said. "Touch my shoulder."

As if mesmerized Heather reached out once more and this time put her hand on his shoulder. As before there was nothing there but a warm electric jolt, but now she didn't draw back. Instead she explored the contours of his upper body from his waist to the top of his head.

To the eye he looked as sturdy and three-dimensional as any man, but to the touch there was no substance, only a force of energy that was shocking in its strength.

Ethan stood quietly and made no protest, until finally she stood back and shook her head wonderingly. "I don't believe it," she whispered. "How can I see you so clearly if you're not here?"

He chuckled. "But I am here," he assured her. "I've only taken a different form. Spirits are pure energy, the body you see is illusion."

"But how—"

He held up a hand to silence her. "I cannot answer any more of your questions. Some answers I have not the words to explain, and others you're not privileged to know yet."

Heather wasn't willing to let it go at that. "All right," she said, trying to be reasonable, "but can you just tell me where you go when you disappear?"

"Nay, I'm sorry but I cannot."

"Then can you tell me if you're always here, on this floor, even when I can't see you?"

A dawning look of comprehension lightened his

face. "Ah, I understand. You want to know if I make myself invisible, then skulk around, spying on you."

Heather shook her head vigorously. "No! Not spying on me," she said emphatically. "You're not that kind of man...uh, being...uh, ghost. Oh, you know what I mean."

Again Ethan chuckled. "Aye, I know, and you spoke the truth on all three tries. I'm not *that kind*. When you cannot see me it is because I'm no longer here."

"But where—"

She watched, fascinated, as he raised his hand and touched one finger to her mouth, effectively stopping her flow of words. There was no pressure, but she felt a hot vibration on the spot where the finger looked to be. "No more, my curious little friend," he said good-naturedly. "Just know that I'm never so far away that I can't come to you when you need me."

He removed his finger, and she experienced a sense of loss.

"I needed you today," she said, looking away from him. "You knew that, didn't you? That's why you came back."

"Aye, I knew. Those great-grandchildren of mine are making you unhappy again."

Heather   gasped.   "Great-grandchildren? You're...?"

He nodded. "Aye, I'm Maxwell and Jocelyn's grandfather from many generations back. They're descendents of my son, Nathaniel, as was their father, and there are times when I'd like to use some good old ghostly discipline on them. However, that is not my way. They have to come to terms with and solve their own problems.''

''Is that why you're here?'' Heather asked, then caught herself. ''Oh, I'm sorry. You told me not to ask any more questions.''

He smiled gently. ''This is one I'm willing to answer,'' he assured her. ''Yes, that is part of the reason I chose to remain here. At one time my family owned much of the land on Beacon Hill, but as it became more valuable, parcels of it were sold over a period of many years. At the time of my demise, my two brothers were anxious to sell more.''

His expression was as thunderous as if he were talking about a recent event, instead of one that had occurred more than two hundred years ago. ''We'd had an excellent offer, but it would have meant selling our birthright. I refused to agree, but when I was shot at Lexington and my sons inherited my share, I was afraid the others would convince them to sell. I couldn't allow that, so I came back to protect my property.''

''Do you mean that the Sheffields own the houses around this one, too?'' Heather asked, finding it difficult to believe that anyone could be rich enough to own so much real estate in this exclusive area.

Ethan shook his head. ''Nay. After the long war with England, the economy was in a shambles. The Hadleigh family, as well as most of the citizens of the Commonwealth, had little left except for their land. Eventually even I had to agree that more of it must be sold. By the middle 1800s when this house was built, there was only the one small lot left.''

"But Max owns a home on Beacon Hill," she pointed out.

"Aye," Ethan agreed. "So do his three brothers, but they were acquired later. Fortunes come and go, and by the turn of the century my descendents were wealthy beyond my imaginings. Now they own property all over these United Colonies and in foreign countries, as well."

A thought occurred to her, but she was hesitant to voice it. Finally after a long silence Ethan asked, "What is troubling you, child?"

She sighed. "It's just...well, it seems to me that you've accomplished what you stayed on here for. Are you...that is, are you *stuck* here now?"

His brow furrowed. "Stuck? I do not stick to anything."

The corners of her mouth turned up in an amused half smile. "No, that's not what I mean. Will you always be a ghost confined to this house. Did you lose your right to go... Oh, darn, now I'm the one who doesn't have the words. What I'm trying to ask is can you still go to heaven?"

Even after all this time she couldn't believe she was having conversations with a spirit! Surely it must be an hallucination. Rational people didn't even see ghosts, let alone talk to them.

His expression softened, and she was engulfed in a bright glow of love. "Ah, my sweet, good-hearted Heather," he murmured in a voice that was choked with emotion. "In the two hundred and sixteen years that I've been here, many who have seen me and been frightened have consigned me to hell, but you are the only mortal who's worried that I might have forfeited my place in heaven. I hasten to assure you that I'm here by choice, and I stay not only because I'm still needed, but also because it pleasures me to watch the proliferation of the seed of my loins."

Heather compressed her lips to keep from giggling. "Proliferation of the seed of my loins" was a tad passé as a household phrase among her male acquaintances, but she knew what he meant. He took pride in watching his descendents emerge and pass his genes along from generation to generation. It was a form of immortality that all humankind longed for.

That evening when the dinner bell rang and Heather went downstairs, she found Max in the living room having a drink with his family. Apparently he'd come to make peace with his mother after their quarrel. Heather wasn't expecting him and was off guard as his uncertain smile sent her heart into fibrillation.

She stopped at the bottom of the stairs, and he walked over to her, looking irresistible in a white linen coat and blue slacks. She was glad she'd finally sent for the rest of her clothes and was wearing a dress, instead of the skirts and blouses she'd mixed and matched ever since she'd been here.

Max's gaze was drawn to the flamingo-pink silky garment that clung to her breasts and waist, then flared gently around her calves. "You look very beautiful," he murmured, and the open admiration in his eyes confirmed the opinion.

She felt the blush of heat on her cheeks and, with an effort, lowered her glance to the area of his blue tie. "Thank you," she said, and it sounded breathless.

He put his hand on her arm. "Are you still upset with me, Heather?" He spoke low, for her ears only.

In spite of her good resolution, he was doing it again, melting her resistance with the hunger that looked out of his eyes and the restrained passion in his voice. She was too inexperienced to play games with him. It could only lead to heartbreak.

Taking a deep breath, she forced an apologetic smile. "No, of course not," she said, and hoped the acting classes she'd taken in college would help her now. "I'm sorry I was rude this noon, but people seem to assume that because I work at home I'm free to come and go as I please. It's a common problem for nannies, as well as writers and artists. It gets irritating at times, and I guess you just caught me in a bad mood."

"If I was insensitive I apologize," he said ruefully. "But since you work for my family and I'm Yvette's uncle, I saw no reason for anyone to object if you and the baby spent a little time with me."

Heather sighed and shook her head. "It doesn't work that way, Max. I'm not free to go on dates or attend social functions, except on my days off, unless I get special permission in advance. The Beauforts pay me well for being available twenty-four hours a day."

Before Max could reply, his mother came over to remind them that it was time to sit down to dinner.

In the dining room Heather took the seat next to Jocelyn, instead of the one on the other side of the table next to Max as she would have preferred. He looked disappointed but said nothing.

During the meal the conversation centered on politics in general and Max's brother, Garrick Sheffield, who was his party's state chairman, in particular.

"I've been trying to get hold of Gary in his office for the past week," Franchot said. "I need to talk to him about some of his investments, but he's never there."

"Same here," commented Max. "I have some partnership matters to discuss with him, but he's been out of town, interviewing possible gubernatorial candidates for the next election. He's never home. That's a hell of a way to live. I swear I don't know how he ever found the time to father that new baby Ruthann is expecting."

Heather was surprised. If Max didn't approve of the life in the fast lane that most politicians adhered to, why was he planning to follow in his brothers' footsteps?

Franchot chuckled. "Oh, I'm sure most of us men can manage to make time for something like that," he said, and winked suggestively at his wife.

Max shrugged. "I suppose," he said doubtfully, "but there must be a more satisfying existence than running yourself ragged, passing laws half the people don't want and campaigning for an office that pays only a fraction of what it costs to get elected."

Mrs. Sheffield looked at her son and frowned. "Really, Maxwell, must you be so cynical?" she said and quickly changed the subject.

Heather had never met Max's brothers. Titus was a U.S. senator and lived most of the time in Washington; Garrick, as she'd just learned, was busy in commonwealth politics; and Lawrence was a working partner in the family law firm, but in the two weeks she'd been living in his mother's home, Heather had never met any of them.

"Does Garrick have other children?" she asked.

"Three," Daphne answered. "Two boys and a girl. I have fourteen grandchildren altogether. Titus has six, three of each gender, and Larry has four, all boys. Then, of course, there's Jocelyn's daughter, and in five more months Garrick and Ruthann will make it fifteen. Also last year one of Titus's daughters presented me with a great-grandson."

Daphne Sheffield may be standoffish with strangers and employees, but the affection in her tone when she spoke of her children and grandchildren told Heather that she loved her large family with a down-to-earth warmth and pride not evident to the casual observer.

"I think that's wonderful," Heather said wistfully. "I never had brothers or sisters, so I've never known what it's like to be part of a real family. When I get married, I'd like to have lots of babies."

Jocelyn glanced at her sideways. "That's a sweet thought, but you'd better make sure you marry a man who can afford to support them. Babies are awful expensive these days."

Heather's dream bubble burst. "Yes, I know," she said sorrowfully. "It's just a beautiful fantasy. I'd never have more children than I could feed, house and educate, which means we'll probably never have more than two."

It was Daphne who spoke then. "By 'we' are you implying that you have a special boyfriend back home in Georgia?" She made no attempt to disguise the hope in her tone.

Heather shook her head. "No, no one. I just meant

me and my husband, who's not likely to make more than an average salary. It takes both a husband and wife working just to keep pace with inflation these days.''

Max scowled as he crumpled his napkin and put it on the table. ''Don't settle for second best, Heather,'' he said impatiently. ''If you want a wealthy husband, then find one. They say it's as easy to love a rich man as a poor one.''

She couldn't tell whether he was angry or just offering advice. ''I'm sure it is,'' she said carefully, ''but I'm not going out husband-hunting. When the right man comes along, I'll know it, and it won't matter to me whether he's rich or poor. I've no intention of marrying a father for my children. When I take those vows before God it will be with someone I love and who loves me. Someone I can't imagine living without. If he shares my desire for a family I'll consider myself fortunate, but if he doesn't I'll marry him anyway, because he will be the most important person in my life.''

She, too, crumpled her napkin and put it on the table, then stood. ''If you will excuse me, I'll go check on Yvette.''

Heather had only been upstairs long enough to look in on the baby and dismiss Velma to go back to her other duties when Max appeared.

''Do I have to make an appointment to see you alone?'' he asked grumpily.

''Of course not,'' she said, striving to keep her tone light. ''If you'll just go back downstairs I'll join you as soon as I've heated Yvette's bottle.''

"But if you bring her along we won't be alone, will we."

She shrugged impatiently. He really could be exasperating when he put his mind to it. "Max, I was hired to take care of the baby, not to entertain you."

"So I've been told," he groused. "Again and again and again, until I'm sick of hearing it. Franchot's buying your services, dammit, not your soul, but if it will make you feel better, I got his permission to come up here and talk to you. Can we go into the parlor and sit down?"

Heather hated it when they quarreled. All she'd ever wanted was to spend time with him. To curl up in his arms and feel his hands caressing her, his lips sending shivers through her, the expression in his eyes telling her she was desirable and he wanted her. Instead, in the interest of keeping her job and her self-respect, she was forced to push him away.

"Yes, if you're sure it's all right with the Beauforts," she answered, and lifted Yvette out of her crib.

"Here, let me carry her." Max took the child from her. "Come on, sunshine," he crooned, "it seems that your nanny and I need you to play chaperon for us."

The baby chuckled happily, and Max grinned. "You're right, it is funny. What other man has a five-month-old child assigned to make sure he doesn't make improper advances to his lady love?"

Heather couldn't stifle a giggle. "Okay, you've made your point," she teased as she picked up a folded cotton pad. "Lead on, but please make an effort to keep your rampant lust under control."

"Oh, my dear," he said with exaggerated suffering. "Have you any idea what a Herculean effort that will take?"

She punched him on the arm and they both laughed as they headed for the parlor.

Ethan was sitting on the sofa when they entered, and he stood and winked at Heather. "I wouldn't want Maxwell to sit on me," he said with a grin. "It would shock the daylights out of him, and he'd never know what caused it."

She laughed harder as a ludicrous picture formed in her mind, but she remembered just in time not to answer him. Instead she unfolded the quilted pad and knelt to lay it on the floor.

"You can put her down here," she told Max as she scattered a few puffy toys that could easily be grabbed by tiny hands. "Put her on her back and watch her turn over."

Max did as he was told, and Yvette promptly rolled over on her stomach and reached for one of the bright rattles.

"See how strong and advanced she is," Heather said, and was aware that she sounded like a proud mother. "Her eye-muscle coordination is quite remarkable for her age, too."

Leaning down she nuzzled the baby's fat little neck and made her laugh with delight, then sat back on her haunches and looked up at Max. "I feel sorry for Jocelyn. She's missing so much by only being with her little daughter an hour or so a day."

He reached for her hand and helped her to stand. "Jocelyn doesn't have to work," he said. "She could stay home with the baby if she wanted to. Her place in the law firm is secure. I'm afraid she likes the idea of having a child, but not the commitment that goes with it.''

"Oh, Max, that's not fair," Heather protested as she sat down on the sofa.

He sat beside her. "When you have children, will you work if you don't have to?"

"No," she answered promptly. "But what's right for me might not be right for many other women."

He was thoughtful for a moment. "That's probably true. Maybe I'm not being fair to Jocelyn. She really doesn't know any other way to raise a child. Our mother didn't work for wages when we were small, but she was involved in every charity and social event in Boston. Still is. She didn't spend much more time with us than Jocelyn does with Yvette. She had nurses and nannies and housekeepers to do all the things that your mother did by herself. Now her grandchildren are being raised the same way."

Heather grinned. "Well, as long as everyone's happy, don't knock it. Constant togetherness isn't all that great, either. There were times when my mother would have given me away to anyone who would take me just to have a few hours alone to do as she pleased."

Max put his arms around her and pulled her close. "I don't believe that for a minute," he murmured into her hair.

His firm hip and thigh pressed against hers, and her breast brushed against the linen of his coat. His scent must have been blended from a witch's aphrodisiac because it made her head swim and her pulses pound. How could she keep her wits about her when her body cried out for his touch every time he got near her?

He put his fingers under her chin and lifted her face to his. "How about a little practice kissing?" he murmured.

"Practice kissing?" She could see the devilment shining in his eyes.

"Well, sure. You're not getting any younger, you know. If you want a house full of babies, you're going to have to start looking for a husband. I'd be happy to help out by teaching you the fine art of canoodling."

She choked back a giggle. "Canoodling?"

"You see?" he said triumphantly. "How can you expect to do it if you don't even know the language?"

He was doing marvelously well at controlling his mirth, but she had trouble keeping a straight face. "I hate to tell you this, Max, but I have been kissed before."

He assumed a schoolmaster expression. "Ah, yes, chaste pecks administered by callow youths."

"Oh, I don't know about that," she said with a seductive leer. "The last man who kissed me seemed pretty experienced. He nearly melted the elastic in my bra."

A roar of laughter from behind Max made Heather shift her gaze over his shoulder to see Ethan convulsed with merriment. "Sorry," he said gleefully, and promptly disappeared.

"Miss Carmichael!" Max's disapproving yelp brought her attention back to him. "Tender young Southern maidens of breeding do not talk about undergarments with gentlemen...."

He paused, and a slow, proud grin replaced his simulated shocked expression. "Your bra, huh?"

In spite of her best efforts, she couldn't keep the corners of her mouth from turning up as she nodded. "Another couple of minutes and it would have been a total loss."

His grin widened, and his arms tightened around her. "In that case I think we can skip the first two lessons and get right on to the third," he said happily.

She arched one eyebrow questioningly. "The third? Are you sure I'm ready for it?"

"I don't know." He groaned. "But I sure as hell am."

In spite of his impatience, he took her mouth gently at first, brushing it with his, back and forth, until she could stand the waiting no longer. She nipped at him and pressed her lips against his as she slid her hands up his chest and stroked the back of his head.

Without breaking the contact, Max shifted her so that she lay across his lap with her feet on the couch, and she clasped him around the neck and opened to his probing tongue. He was right; she had been a novice before he taught her the excitement of this seductively intimate form of...what had he called it? Canoodling.

She trembled as one of his hands curved around her breast while the other settled on her calf. He squeezed her nylon-covered leg, then glided his palm up to cover her knee before he broke off the kiss and raised his head. "Sweetheart," he murmured. "Isn't it about time to put our little chaperon to bed? I'm not used to being watched."

Heather's eyes flew open, and she sat up and glanced down to see Yvette lying on her stomach at the edge of the pad, looking at them and drooling from a wide, toothless smile.

"Oh, good heavens," she muttered, and scurried off the couch. "It certainly is time to give her a bottle and put her to bed. How could I have been so...so..."

"Calm down," Max said reasonably, "we haven't done anything wrong. She's apparently not very hungry or she'd be yelling, and she certainly doesn't look sleepy. In fact, she seems to be highly entertained."

He chuckled and picked the baby up off the floor, then grimaced. "Uh-oh," he said as he removed one hand from her well-padded bottom, "I'm afraid she's in rather dire need of a dry diaper, and I'm going to have to send my jacket to the cleaners."

"Carry her into the nursery and put her on the changing table," Heather instructed, "then you'll have to leave."

"Leave? There's no need for me to leave. I'll give her the bottle, then you can put her to bed and we can go back to what we were doing." He grinned suggestively.

"Oh, no, we can't," she said, and preceded him through the nursery door. "I can see why the Beauforts don't want you up here with me. They're paying me to take care of Yvette, not to neck in the parlor with you. Now, please, go home before I get into real trouble."

Max deposited the squirming little bundle on the changing table and buckled her down so she couldn't fall off. "Heather, be reasonable," he said as she took dry garments from the chest of drawers. "You're entitled to have your evenings free unless notified in advance that you'll be needed. I know. I negotiated your contract, remember?''

He moved to stand at the top of the table and make room for her at the side where it was more convenient to maneuver as she changed the baby.

"I understand that," she said, and reached out to unfasten the pins, "but that's not the point. Think, Max, if you had a nanny caring for your child, would you allow her to have men visitors at any hour of the day or night? I wouldn't."

"Neither would I," he answered, "but it's only eight o'clock, hardly the middle of the night, and I'm not just a man visitor. I'm the baby's uncle, it's my family home and I have permission from your employer to be here."

Heather had to admit that technically he was right, but she also knew that making out with him up here in the nursery area would be an abuse of her duties as an employee. Especially when his mother and sister had made it plain that they disapproved of any type of relationship between her and Max.

She had a budding career as a nanny, but there was no future for her with Maxwell Sheffield.

Removing the wet diaper, she put it in the hamper the laundry service provided and replaced it with a snowy-white clean one. "Please," she pleaded, knowing that she couldn't win the argument with logic. "I just wouldn't feel right about it."

He sighed and handed her a can of baby powder. "All right, if that's what you want I'll leave, but tomorrow and Sunday are your days off. Will you spend them with me? We'll take a ride on a swan boat in the public gardens."

Heather often wheeled Yvette through the public gardens on their daily walks. It was a haven of green trees, flowering shrubs, quiet walkways and bright blossoms across Charles Street from the west end of the Boston Common. The centerpiece was a picturesque lake with long, flat-bottomed sight-seeing boats featuring a large sculpture of a white swan at one end.

She had promised herself a ride on one of the swan boats during a day off, and nothing would please her more than to share that ride with Max, but a vision of Mrs. Sheffield's icy disapproval made her hesitate.

She secured the diaper with the safety pins. "Max, you know how your mother and sister feel about me dating you." There was regret in her tone. "I'm sorry, but it's best if we don't go out together."

"Mother and Jocelyn have nothing to say about it," he snapped. "We're both adults, and they have no control over you on your days off. Besides, the park is filled with people on weekends, and the police frown on couples making love publicly on the grass or under the bushes. I promise to bring you back home untouched."

"Untouched?" she queried skeptically.

His glare softened to a grin. "Probably not," he admitted. "You know I can't keep my hands off you. Maybe unsullied is a better word."

She felt the weight of sorrow as she raised the baby up and slid a soft cotton nightgown over her bobbing little head. "Unfortunately words have little effect when emotions get out of control," she said sadly. "We're playing with fire, Max. I know that's an old game for you, and I'm sure you're delighted each time the fire wins, but I was raised with a different set of values. If this goes any further I'm the one who will be hurt, and I've had all the grief in my life that I can handle.''

She laid Yvette back down and snapped the fastenings on the gown. ''Please, just leave me alone. Give me a chance to find that nice, safe, reliable husband who will father the two children we'll be able to afford.''

She picked up the baby and turned away from him to put her in her crib. When she straightened up and looked around, Max was gone.

Chapter Eight

Max hurried down the stairs and left the house with only a curt goodbye to his mother. He'd driven over by himself in the Jaguar and given Nick the night off since he'd anticipated spending most of it with Heather. Not in her bed, but hopefully getting to know each other very well in the parlor.

He unlocked the car door and slid in under the wheel. That last thought was a crock and he knew it. It was probably just as well that she'd thrown him out. If she'd shown any interest at all in making love with him, he wouldn't have been able to resist no matter how strong his good intentions.

He turned the key in the engine and it sprang to life as his thoughts continued. There was a warm, loving aura about Heather that he found irresistible, and no matter how many times he vowed to stay away from her something always pulled him back. She'd taken up residence in his very soul, tormenting him by day and haunting him at night.

He was becoming obsessive about her, and that scared him. His mother was right; he would seduce her if he got half a chance, and then how could he live with his conscience?

He backed out of the driveway and maneuvered the Jag up the alley and turned into the street. It wasn't as if he was thinking of marrying her. He'd always known that when he took that step it would be with a woman handpicked for her credentials to be the wife of a rising young politician, just as his father and older brothers had. If he loved her, so much the better, but if not it was no big deal.

At least, it hadn't been until he met Heather Carmichael, the gracious little nanny with the radiant smile that made him happy, the tender touch that made him ache for more and the responsive libido that drove him wild.

He had to admit that he was taking unfair advantage of her to satisfy his own needs. She'd gently forced him to acknowledge his distaste for the wheeling and dealing that was common among politicians, the depth of his desire to be loved for himself and not his money or position. He almost purred with contentment every time she held him and stroked him in such innocent places as his face, his hair and his back. He hadn't known how erogenous those places could be until she'd touched them and brought them to throbbing life.

He frowned as a thought occurred to him. Females had been doing those things to him ever since he was sixteen years old, and it had been pleasant but certainly not addicting.

Why was it only Heather's caress that kept him yearning and coming back for more?

Heather spent a restless night trying not to think of Max, but unable to push him out of her mind or her heart. She'd never dreamed that the breakup of such a short and tenuous relationship could hurt so badly. It was unreal. Everyone knew that it takes weeks, even months, to truly know another person.

Her feelings for Max couldn't be love; she hadn't known him long enough. It had to be a delayed teenage infatuation. She'd heard that they could be very intense, and that when they ended, the pain was real. Well, her pain was real, all right, and she doubted that it was going away anytime soon. She'd just have to learn to deal with it.

Heather was awake at six o'clock when she heard Yvette tuning up to demand her breakfast. Although Saturday was one of her days off, she got up and changed and fed the baby before her fussing woke Jocelyn. Since Heather couldn't sleep, anyway, she might as well let her employer enjoy a little extra.

Thanks to her own stubbornness and outdated moral values Heather had no plans for the weekend. She might as well put in some volunteer time with her little charge, although she knew Max would insist that she was letting the Beauforts take advantage of her if he knew.

By the time Yvette finished the bottle, she was wide-awake and playful, so Heather dressed in a pair of white shorts and a white scoop-necked cotton knit shirt. After brushing her hair up off her neck, she twisted it into a neat coil on top of her head and anchored it with long black bobby pins so the baby couldn't grab it and pull.

When she was ready she scooped up Yvette and the floor pad and walked, barefoot, across the hall and into the parlor where Ethan was waiting for her as she'd hoped he'd be. He was perched on top of the pianoforte with his legs drawn up and crossed in front of him in an attitude of meditation.

It startled her. Except for his lack of color he looked so much like an ordinary man dressed in a costume that she was unprepared for his ability to go places and assume positions that no mortal could.

The pianoforte was a fragile old instrument that would collapse under the weight of a man his size, and it was so narrow at the top that only his backside fit on it. There was nothing but air under his crossed legs, but he seemed perfectly comfortable and at ease.

A welcoming smile lit his face, and he pointed a finger at the baby in her arms. "Good morning, my pretty little granddaughter," he said, and Yvette squealed with delight and held her arms out to him. "Ah, would that I could bounce you on my knee, but that pleasure is denied me."

He withdrew his hand and looked at Heather. "It's about time you came in here to tell me about your tiff with Maxwell. Why do you keep sending him away, girl?"

Heather groaned. It was easy to tell that he and Max were related. They were both maddening at times.

"You promised that you wouldn't spy on me," she said crossly, "so how do you know I sent him away?"

His smile disappeared. "I do not have to be there to know when you are unhappy. I know Maxwell is unhappy, too, but I do not go to his home."

A thought occurred to her. "If you know his state of mind, then tell me how he feels about me. Does he love me? Is there any chance he might want to marry me?"

Ethan propped his elbow on one knee and rested his chin on his raised fist. "I cannot tell you that, but if you were just a bit more perceptive you could see for yourself."

Disappointed, Heather knelt down and spread the pad on the floor, then deposited the baby on it. "I am perceptive," she informed him, "and it's pretty plain that he's attracted to me, but not enough to marry me."

Ethan frowned. "Is it your hope that by refusing him your company you will spur him to propose marriage?"

Heather shook her head. "No, of course not. It's my hope that by refusing him my company, as you so quaintly put it, he'll go away and leave me alone."

"And so he did," Ethan replied. "So why are you sad?"

She sighed and sat down on the floor with her legs drawn up in front of her. "Because I'm afraid I'm in love, and people in love are seldom logical. I don't really want him to go away. I want him to love me, too."

"Be not so impatient," Ethan advised. "Give the poor boy time..."

A voice from behind Heather made her jump. "Heather. Who are you talking to?"

It was Jocelyn, standing in the archway looking perplexed and more than a little apprehensive.

Heather scrambled to her feet, her heart pounding with anxiety. "Jocelyn! I...I mean Mrs. Beaufort. I didn't hear you coming," she finished lamely.

Jocelyn walked into the room and looked around. "Obviously not. You were too busy talking. At first I thought you were on the telephone so I stood just out of sight for a few minutes, but it seemed too much like eavesdropping so I moved closer to make myself known."

Again she looked around, her gaze sweeping right past Ethan and settling on Heather. "There's no telephone in your hand, and no other adult in the room." Her tone was accusing. "Do you make a habit of talking to yourself?"

Heather realized that Jocelyn had only heard her side of the conversation since she could neither see nor hear Ethan. She tried to think back to what she'd said, but the shock of being discovered talking to a ghost had driven everything from her mind.

Dear God, how was she going to explain?

She looked at Ethan, but he just sat there watching. Damn him! Why didn't he help her?

"N-n-no," she stammered. "I wasn't talking to myself. I was..." Her glance fell on Yvette who was lying on her back and happily counting her fingers. "I was talking to the baby," she finished, hoping the other woman would believe her.

That hope was quickly dashed. "No, you weren't," Jocelyn said grimly. "I've heard you talk to Yvette many times, and the conversation you were just having wasn't aimed at an infant. I'm sorry, Heather, but

I'm going to insist that you explain what's going on. Do you have imaginary companions that you talk to?''

Heather was numb with alarm. She knew that Jocelyn was wondering if their newly hired nanny was a weirdo. Unless Heather could give a satisfactory explanation for what she had to admit looked like strange behavior, the Beauforts would not only fire her but report her to the college and make sure she never worked with children again.

She couldn't blame them. She'd feel the same way if it were her child's nanny who talked to unseen friends!

In desperation she looked pleadingly at Ethan whose expression revealed his sorrow and regret. ''Tell her you'll explain the incident, but you want Maxwell present since he is your attorney,'' he said somberly.

''But how...?'' she started to answer, then realized what she was doing. Snapping her mouth shut, she turned to Jocelyn instead.

''No, Mrs. Beaufort, I don't have imaginary companions,'' she said carefully, ''but I do owe you and the others in this house an explanation. I'd like to talk to you and Mr. Beaufort, and Mrs. Sheffield, but in my own best interest I must have Max present, also, since he did volunteer to be my attorney.''

Jocelyn looked even more apprehensive. ''I see,'' she said, and stooped to pick her daughter up off the mat. ''I'll contact Max and let you know when he gets here. Meanwhile I'll keep the baby with me, and I'd appreciate it if you'd wait up here until I call you.''

She turned and walked away carrying Yvette.

Heather waited until she was sure she couldn't be heard, then spoke to Ethan. "What am I going to tell them?" she wailed.

He looked thoughtful. "This is all my fault," he answered regretfully. "I should have known she was approaching. 'Twas uncommonly careless of me, and now I've put you at risk. The only recourse is to tell them the truth."

She gasped. "You mean tell them about you?"

"Aye, and there's naught I can do to help you this time. 'Tis permitted that I meddle in insignificant things such as the intrusion of Miss Zimmerman, but I cannot change your destiny."

"But this has nothing to do with destiny," she insisted.

"Aye, it does my dear," he assured her. "The outcome of this blunder will touch many lives. I can only stay with you and maybe coach you a bit in small things."

"Would you, please?" There was urgency in her tone.

"I would never abandon you when you need me," he said softly. "You are as dear to me as a daughter."

Heather felt tears welling in her eyes. "Thank you. I feel as though you've become the father I lost."

He nodded. "Aye. That is why you see and hear me. You were searching for the father who died so unexpectedly, and therefore you were sensitive and open to spirits. Had he not been taken from you so recently, or if you had not missed him so keenly, you would never have been aware of me."

Heather shivered and felt goose bumps on her arms

as his words touched a cord. "Can you...that is, do you know if my father..."

She couldn't go on. She wasn't even sure she wanted an answer to her question.

"Nay," Ethan said abruptly, and she felt his unspoken reproof.

She hung her head. "I'm sorry. I shouldn't have asked."

During the uncomfortable silence that followed, the telephone rang. It was Jocelyn asking Heather to meet with Max and the rest of the family at eleven o'clock in Daphne Sheffield's office on the second floor.

When she put the phone down, Ethan was gone.

Exactly at eleven o'clock Heather started downstairs. It had occurred to her after Ethan disappeared, and she could no longer question him, that he'd told her he never roamed below the fourth floor of the house. She'd never seen him anywhere but the parlor, so how could he be with her at the meeting since it was being held on the second floor?

Having resigned herself to facing the Sheffield family without his support, she'd tried to compose a believable story in her mind about Ethan's presence, but she was too upset to concentrate. How did one explain a ghost without appearing to have slipped over into the netherworld of madness?

She'd better find a way because her whole future depended on it.

The sound of voices coming from the second floor reached her as she descended the stairs, and when she arrived at Daphne Sheffield's office, they were all gathered there, waiting for her.

Max was standing just outside the door, apparently watching for Heather. When she appeared, he hurried to her and took both her hands in his. "Honey, what's going on?" The beautiful green eyes that had the power to hypnotize her were now filled with bewilderment. "Jocelyn says you're behaving irrationally and want me to act as your legal representative before you'll explain why."

The grip of his hands on hers was reassuring, but she couldn't help but wonder if this was the last time he'd touch her so lovingly. It was bad enough that she was too young, too unsophisticated and too low class for a Sheffield wife, but he'd probably do a disappearing act even quicker than Ethan's when he discovered that she was an unbalanced oddball who talked to ghosts, as well.

"I'm not irrational," she told him, "but I can see why Jocelyn thinks I am. Silly though it seems, I need someone to protect me from the truth...."

It belatedly occurred to her that it was asking a lot of Max to pit himself against his family in such a serious situation. Negotiating her terms of employment with his sister was one thing, but defending the nanny of his own beloved little niece against the charge that she was unfit, which is what this was all about, was another matter altogether.

She withdrew her hands from his and sought his gaze. "Max, if you'd rather not get involved I'll understand. This really isn't a matter of law..."

He frowned, but took her arm. "Don't talk nonsense. Of course I'll protect you," he said, and led her into the room.

The buzz of conversation died as they walked in,

and Franchot, Jocelyn and Daphne turned to look at them. There was also another man there, tall and handsome with enough of the Sheffield features that Heather identified him as one of Max's older brothers.

It was Jocelyn who introduced him. "Heather, I don't believe you've met my brother, Lawrence. We've asked him to sit in as both a member of the family and as an attorney."

Lawrence put out his hand with an engaging smile and gripped Heather's. "I'm sorry we haven't met before, Heather, but my wife and I have been vacationing in France and only returned a couple of days ago."

He must have sensed her anxiety, and his expression turned to one of concern. "Come now, don't be nervous. I'm sure you have a logical explanation for your behavior. Let's all sit down and talk about it."

"Fine," said Max as he seated Heather on the leather sofa, then sat down beside her. "But before she says anything I want to know what the charges against her are."

Daphne, who was sitting in her executive chair behind the desk, looked up sharply. "There are no charges," she said. "We just want her to explain who she was holding a conversation with this morning when she was all alone in the fourth-floor parlor. I can't think why she feels she needs an attorney present."

Max looked annoyed. "She was probably talking on the telephone."

"No, she wasn't," Jocelyn interrupted, then told those assembled what she saw and heard when she went up to the nursery to check on the baby. "She was sitting on the floor nowhere near a telephone, and the only other person in the parlor was Yvette," she concluded. "You have to admit that holding a one-way conversation with yourself is a little strange."

Heather took a deep breath and plunged in. "I wasn't talking to myself," she said quietly, "and neither do I have an imaginary companion as you suggested this morning. I was talking to Ethan, and he was sitting on the pianoforte."

"Who's Ethan?" said several voices in unison.

Heather felt beads of perspiration trickling between her breasts, and she twisted her hands in her lap. How could she possibly tell them the truth? No one would believe her, and they'd think she was crazy.

All eyes were on her, but her mind had gone blank when a blessedly familiar voice spoke to her. "Be not afraid, Mistress Heather. Just start at the beginning and tell them everything you know about me."

Her gaze flew to the hallway from which the voice had come, and there was Ethan leaning against the doorjamb with his arms folded and his ankles crossed. She gasped with surprise and opened her mouth to ask how he'd gotten off the fourth floor, but he put his finger to his lips and shook her head.

"Don't talk to me, talk to them," he warned, then answered her unspoken question. "I said I *didn't* leave the fourth floor, not that I couldn't."

Ethan's presence brought back some of her self-confidence, and she turned to face her audience. "Ethan is the ghost who resides in the parlor on the fourth floor," she said as calmly as she could manage.

The expressions of everyone in the room were almost identical. Astonishment followed by shocked disbelief.

Max blanched and looked ill, but was the first to find his voice. "My God, Heather! Don't say another word." He looked around at the startled members of his family. "I need time to talk to Heather alone," he said, his tone raspy with dismay. "If you'll excuse us…"

He started to rise, but she caught him by the arm. "No, Max. I know you're doing what I asked and trying to protect me, but this has been brought up now and it needs to be discussed."

He put his hand over hers and spoke in a husky whisper. "Honey, trust me. I know what I'm doing. If you admit to talking to ghosts it'll be professional suicide. Now come on, let's—"

Her restraint on his arm tightened. "I appreciate your advice and concern," she assured him, "but we can't just lock Ethan up in a closet and pretend he's not here. He *is* here, Max. He was here before this house was ever built. His family used to own the land both under and around it."

Max's face was ashen as his anguished gaze roamed over her during the strained silence that followed her pronouncement. He apparently saw that she was adamant, that she was unalterably convinced that she saw a ghost who spoke to her. With a moan of despair he reached out and took her in his arms.

"All right, sweetheart," he said in a voice still hollow with shock. "Tell us all about it. When did you discover that we had a ghost?"

Although he tried to disguise it, his tone told her

that he was humoring her but didn't for a moment accept the concept of a spirit in the house.

Heather settled in his embrace with her back angled against his chest and looked at the family members gathered there. Their doubtful expressions made it plain that they thought she was hallucinating, but they seemed willing to listen.

She was grateful for that, but it was Max her heart went out to. He was more deeply affected than she'd expected him to be. She'd just put an unbridgeable chasm between them, deeper and wider than anything that had made their relationship implausible before, and once more she felt his pain.

Maybe he did care for her, after all.

"You must understand that I'm not a spiritualist," she began. "I neither raise ghosts nor exorcise them. I've never believed in spirits and haven't had any interest in reading or hearing about them. No one could have been more surprised or disbelieving than I when Ethan first appeared to me...."

As Ethan had advised, she started her story with the engulfing warmth she'd felt the first time she stepped onto the fourth floor of the house, and told them everything that had transpired between her and the ghost from the time he first appeared, up to advising them that he was standing in the doorway right now watching.

She explained the clever way that Ethan had frightened Miss Zimmerman and driven her from the house, and told of her own anger with him afterward. She hoped the story would add credence to her tale since all of them except Lawrence had witnessed the results of the episode, and Franchot did respond.

"Heather, you say that this ghost is here in the room. I'm sure we would all be convinced of his presence if he'd do some of his tricks for us now." He sounded truly willing to be persuaded if she could just give some visible evidence. "We could hardly disbelieve if articles began floating around in the air."

She looked at Ethan, but he shook his head sadly. "I cannot. They have to be open to me before I can appear to them in this matter."

Heather had known what his answer would be. He'd told her this before, but for a moment she'd hoped...

She directed her attention back to Franchot. "He says he can't interfere this time. That it isn't within his power to change my destiny. I guess what he means is that you have to accept what I'm telling you on faith without a miracle."

When none of them indicated they were able to do that, she continued her story. From time to time she glanced at Ethan, hoping for some help, but he just stood propped against the doorway, nodding encouragement but offering no comment.

It seemed to her that it took a long time to tell of her experiences. Jocelyn broke in once to angrily deny that her small daughter could see a spirit, and Lawrence, a devoutly religious man, found conflicts between his church's dogma concerning the afterlife and some of the things Ethan said and did.

Heather had no answers for them; she could only insist that she was repeating what had happened.

Max said nothing, just sat there holding her and listening until she'd finished. "I cannot prove any of this," she concluded, "but I hope that those of you who've come to know me reasonably well will accept that I wouldn't deliberately lie to you. However, if you doubt my sanity, there's probably no way I can convince you otherwise."

There was silence in the room until Daphne broke it. "You say this ghost insists that he's an ancestor of the Sheffields?" Her tone was more businesslike than skeptical.

"Yes, he did."

"If that's true, then we should be able to verify it," she said. "I have the family genealogy that goes back to the *Mayflower*. Someone in my husband's family had it traced years ago. I glanced through it once, but didn't pay attention to names. We can see if there's an Ethan Hadleigh listed."

For the first time Heather's spirits rose. "But that's wonderful! Is it here in the house?"

Daphne nodded and stood. "Yes, if I remember right, it's in that file." She gestured toward the metal cabinet in the corner and stood. "I'll get the key."

She left the room but was back in a minute. After unlocking the file cabinet and rummaging through it for a short time, she smiled triumphantly and extracted a legal-size binder.

She put it on the desk and opened it. "Now let's see," she said, running her finger down several pages while Lawrence, Jocelyn and Franchot crowded around to look over her shoulder.

Max didn't move, and Heather was in no state to do anything but pray.

Finally Daphne exclaimed, "Ah, here it is," and began to read. "Ethan Miles Hadleigh. Born: 1734. Died: 1775. Son of John William Hadleigh and Elizabeth Wordsworth Hadleigh. Wife: Prudence Smith Hadleigh. Sons: Nathaniel Thomas, George William and Miles Geoffery. Daughter: Priscilla Ann Hadleigh Stone.''

Heather tingled with excitement as she pulled out of Max's embrace and turned to look at him. ''That confirms everything Ethan told me,'' she said joyfully, and wondered why he didn't look happier.

It was Lawrence who burst her bubble. ''I'm afraid it doesn't prove anything except that you are familiar with the Sheffield family tree.''

She stared at him. ''But...?''

''The information in that binder is a matter of public record,'' Max explained. ''Any good genealogy service could have retrieved it for you. Also this copy was right here in the office where anyone could have gotten to it.''

Heather cringed from the blow of his words. ''Are you accusing me of...of setting up some elaborate scheme to make you think there's a ghost when there really isn't?'' She felt humiliated and betrayed. ''Why would I do a thing like that? I'd have nothing to gain and everything to lose!''

''No!'' he said emphatically. ''I'm not accusing you of anything. I don't doubt but that you believe that you see and talk with this phantom...''

''I don't *believe* that I do,'' she said desperately, ''I *know* that I do. Ethan is not a figment of my imagination, he's an actual manifestation of an ancestor of yours. I can understand your reluctance to accept that, but to think that I'd actually plan to deceive you...''

''Not deceive us, honey,'' he insisted. ''I'm sure none of us thinks that, but let's face it, the Sheffield family has no secrets. Everything we do is chronicled in the newspapers, magazines and on television. It's possible that you read or heard about this many-great-grandfather of ours and forgot about it, only to have the information resurface once you started living here and experienced something that made you think we had a ghost upstairs. These old houses creak and make frightening noises—''

''Oh, Max, it's not like that at all.'' She groaned. ''Ghosts don't seem to be all that uncommon in New England.'' She looked around the assembled group. ''Haven't any of you ever had a friend or acquaintance who claimed to have experienced one?''

Jocelyn answered. ''Our family has lived on this property almost ever since the first pilgrim stepped off the *Mayflower*, and for as far back as any of us here can remember, there's been no mention of anything occult.''

She stood and started toward the doorway. ''You say this Ethan is here now?''

Heather nodded.

''Then let's see if I can make contact with him.''

She reached out and waved her hands in the air while Ethan stood where he was without moving. After a few swipes Jocelyn's hand passed across his head, and she uttered a little cry of surprise and jerked her arm back. ''Ouch,'' she said, and rubbed her palm against her hip. ''I didn't realize there was so much static electricity in the air.''

''You slapped him,'' Heather murmured absently.

For a moment Jocelyn looked startled, then her expression softened and she walked over to sit beside Heather and Max on the sofa. ''Heather,'' she said gently. "If you were the housekeeper, or the maid, or the gardener, I'd just give up trying to convince you otherwise and humor this rather charming aberration of yours, but you're my child's nanny. You have total responsibility for her when Franchot or I are not around, and for that reason I can't just shrug this off. If you have any suggestions, I'll gladly listen to them."

From across the room Ethan spoke. "Ask her to bring a clairvoyant to the house."

Heather blinked. A psychic! A person especially sensitive to supernatural influences. Surely such a one would see Ethan! Why hadn't she thought of that herself?

She looked at him and smiled her gratitude, then turned back to Jocelyn, but before she could make the suggestion, Max spoke. "We could call in a parapsychologist. I'm almost certain there's one on the faculty at Tufts, and probably Brandeis, too," he said, mentioning two well-known private universities in the area.

Heather was flabbergasted. Was that his own idea, or had he picked up on Ethan's request.

"That's an excellent thought," Daphne exclaimed, "and now that you mention it, I can even suggest one. Iris Unger's daughter, Kathryn, is a parapsychologist and has her own practice. You remember Kathryn, don't you, Lawrence? You two were in high school together."

Larry nodded. "Yeah, I remember her." He grinned. "She used to tell me I had an interesting aura, but I thought she was just coming on to me."

"Iris was talking about her just a couple of months

ago at a meeting of the D.A.R.," Daphne explained. "She said that Kathryn is attracting national attention by helping the police solve some of their missing-persons cases."

Daphne reached for the telephone. "I'll call Iris and get her number."

When contacted, Kathryn Unger was willing to help but wouldn't be available until the following afternoon, Sunday. Heather was disappointed. She wanted to get the whole thing over with, one way or the other, but Max seemed relieved as they left the office through the doorway from which Ethan had disappeared as soon as the appointment with Dr. Unger was finalized.

"I'm not going to leave you here to mope," Max told her. "We'll have lunch at the Harbor Terrace and then take that ride on the swan boat in the public gardens."

She opened her mouth to protest, but he put his hand over it. "This time I'm not going to take no for an answer," he warned with a twinkle in his eye, "so don't bother to say it."

He removed his hand, and she grinned in spite of her anxiety. "I was just going to say that I'd have to change my clothes."

Looking her over slowly, his gaze lingered on her long, bare legs. "Must you?" he asked huskily.

"I'm afraid so," she said as they headed for the stairway. "Shall I meet you downstairs?"

He nodded. "Yeah, and, Heather, pack a few things in a bag and bring it with you. You're staying at my place tonight."

She gasped. "Who gave you the right to make that decision?" she asked. "I have no intention—"

He held up his hand. "Slow down, honey, I didn't mean that the way it sounded. I have plenty of extra bedrooms and they all have locks on the doors. You can choose any one you want, and Opal will be there to chaperone. I absolutely guarantee that I won't even hold your hand if you don't want me to. I just want to get you out of this house until tomorrow afternoon."

Chapter Nine

Heather awakened the following morning snuggled between cream-colored satin sheets, with a light-weight navy-blue satin quilt covering her and goose-down-filled pillows beneath her head. Drowsily she wondered if she'd died and gone to heaven during the night, and then she remembered that Max was sleeping in the room next to hers.

That invigorating thought brought her to full awareness, and she sat up and looked around. Last night she'd had too many other things on her mind to give more than passing attention to the lamplit room, but now with the bright sunlight streaming in the windows she could fully appreciate the gleaming brass bed, the solid mahogany furniture and the decorator colors of cream accented with navy and red.

Masculine enough for a bachelor's home, but feminine enough to please a woman guest. Were there many of those?

She pushed the disturbing thought from her mind. Possibly there were, but it was for certain none of her business.

Drawing up her legs, she wrapped her arms around the shins and rested her chin on her knees. Max had really meant it when he'd said she'd be safe spending the night with him. He literally hadn't touched her, except to take her arm or capture her attention, since she'd left him yesterday afternoon to change her clothes before going out to lunch.

The Harbor Terrace, on the second floor of the Marriott Long Wharf Hotel where he'd taken her, had a spectacular view of the Boston Harbor, and the food served in the glass-enclosed semicircular restaurant was mouth watering. She could still taste the crisply sautéed crabmeat cakes with the spicy sauce that was like nothing she'd ever eaten before, not to mention the positively decadent dessert. Something with cinnamon-coated tortillas, ice cream and thick caramel sauce topped with sliced bananas and fresh mint.

After that, they'd gone next door to view the sea life at the New England aquarium, then on to the public gardens where they'd floated lazily around the lake in one of the quaint swan boats.

Max had kept her entertained with funny little anecdotes and small talk, and she'd had a marvelous time, even almost managing to put the painful business of that morning out of her mind, until they'd come home to his house.

It was then that the strain returned and they ran out of conversation. Max appeared not to be any more eager to talk about her ghost than she was, and they didn't have anything else to discuss. After all, what could the youngest scion of the powerful Sheffield family, who all his life had had everything money and influence could buy, have in common with the only daughter of a lovable, absentminded poet who barely earned enough to make the house payment and keep them decently fed and clothed?

Nothing, that's what, and they both knew it. Add to that the fact that she saw and talked to ghosts, while he was a hardheaded realist who didn't believe in anything that couldn't be proved or worked out mathematically, and it was no wonder that even the strong physical attraction between them wasn't enough.

Not enough for Max, anyway. He'd tried, but after Opal had served them a light supper and retired to her rooms, they'd found it more comfortable to turn on the television and watch it, him in one chair and her in another some distance away, than to talk.

By ten o'clock she'd been exhausted, and excused herself to go to bed. Even then he hadn't made an effort to kiss her good-night, or even walk upstairs with her. He'd just smiled and told her that his room was next to hers and if she needed anything to call him.

She needed something, all right. She needed his arms around her, his mouth hungry on hers, his assurance that everything was going to be all right...

But, of course, everything wasn't going to be all right. Heather seriously doubted that the Beauforts would allow her to care for Yvette after this, even if the parapsychologist could convince them that she wasn't crazy. The best she could hope for was that they wouldn't report her "strangeness" to the college and make it impossible for her to ever work with children again.

Max, too, wasn't going to commit himself to a woman who was not only unsuitable, but also bewitched. No, this time the truth hadn't set her free. It had bound her with the specter of eccentricity and changed the course of her life.

No responsible parent would hire a wacko to look after the youngsters!

Heather got out of bed and slipped into the jeans and shirt she'd brought with her. A touch of lipstick and a few strokes of the brush through her hair completed her grooming, and she went downstairs in search of either Max or Opal.

She found them both in the kitchen where Max was lingering over a cup of coffee while Opal bustled around fixing breakfast. "Mmm," Heather said breathing in deeply, "nothing smells better than bacon and coffee early in the morning."

Max smiled and stood. He, too, was dressed in comfortable jeans and pullover shirt, and he looked so appealing that it brought a lump to her throat. "Good morning, Heather," he said, and pulled a chair out for her next to him. "You look bright eyed and rested. Did you sleep well?"

She smiled in return. "I fell into bed last night and didn't surface again until about twenty minutes ago."

Opal served them bacon, eggs, bran muffins and orange juice, then sat down to eat with them. With her there to keep it going, the conversation flowed, and Heather realized how much she'd missed the easy camaraderie of breakfast at the kitchen table. The morning meal at the Sheffield-Beaufort residence was an elaborate buffet in the stiff formal dining room.

When they'd finished, Max excused himself to go over some business papers in his study, and Heather insisted on helping Opal with the dishes. She didn't see him again until it was time for them to leave for the appointment with the parapsychologist at his mother's house.

Heather and Max arrived at the Sheffield family home just moments before Dr. Kathryn Unger was ushered into the first-floor parlor. She was an attractive woman in her late thirties, tall and slender with short blond hair and brown eyes. Her only concession to the image people usually associate with a psychic was the large chunky necklace, bracelets and earrings she wore with her black jumpsuit.

The family members greeted her warmly, but before anyone could introduce her to Heather, Kathryn turned to her and put out her hand. Heather automatically took it, and Kathryn said, "You're the one who's had the paranormal experience."

There was a collective gasp from everyone since Dr. Unger had refused to listen to any explanation on the phone yesterday, other than that they appeared to have a psychic phenomenon that needed interpretation.

Heather felt a tiny shiver at the back of her neck and withdrew her hand. "Yes, how did you know?"

The other woman smiled. "I recognized a fellow psychic."

"But I'm not," Heather protested. "I've never even believed in ghosts."

"Then this is your first experience?"

"And my last," Heather fervently promised.

This time Kathryn laughed. "That may be, but don't count on it," she said. "I'll need to know your name and your relationship to this house."

Max walked over to stand by Heather. "Her name is Heather Carmichael," he said. "She's Jocelyn's child's nanny."

Kathryn nodded. "Fine. Now, Heather, where did you have this experience?"

"On the fourth floor. It's strongest in the parlor. I—"

Kathryn held up her hand. "No, don't give me any details, just answer my questions as briefly as possible. I want you to go up there with me." She turned to the others. "You're all welcome to come along."

They all started up the stairs, with Heather and Kathryn in the lead. When they were about halfway up the third flight, Kathryn stopped and just stood there for a moment.

"Is this where you first felt the warmth?" she asked.

Again Heather was shaken. "How did you know about the warmth?" she blurted, then caught herself. "A...a little farther up," she stammered. "Just before I stepped onto the floor."

"I feel it, too," Dr. Unger explained as they went up the remaining steps. "Oh, yes, it's very strong up here," she exclaimed as they reached the top.

There were murmurs of astonishment and denial from the others as they walked toward the parlor. Ethan was standing at the side of the pianoforte waiting for them. Heather hadn't seen him since he'd disappeared from the doorway of Mrs. Sheffield's office yesterday, but he looked past her and didn't speak. Dr. Unger stood in the center of the room and looked around as the rest of them seated themselves.

No one spoke as Kathryn scanned the room again, this time slowly. "I'm aware of a presence," she said finally. "It's male and from an earlier time in history. It's a long-entrenched spirit. A benign one. I feel no animosity."

Again there were mutterings of disbelief from the family, but Heather was too engrossed to care. "Can't you see him?" she asked.

Kathryn shook her head. "No, but I sense that it's because he's resisting me. Does he speak?"

"Oh, my, yes," Heather answered. "That's what got me into trouble. He—"

"Not yet," Kathryn interrupted. "I'll let you tell me your story later, but right now I don't want to be distracted. Does he have a name?"

The woman's way of talking about Ethan as though he couldn't hear or understand her irritated Heather. "Of course he has a name," she snapped. "He's not just a blob of ectoplasm, he's a fully formed man."

As soon as the words were out she knew she'd overreacted. Ethan was definitely not a fully formed man, and she'd better remember that before they had her locked up with the rest of the crazies.

"I'm sorry," she said. "This is all very upsetting…"

"I understand that," Kathryn said gently. "Will you tell me his name?"

Heather nodded. "It's Ethan Hadleigh."

Once more Kathryn's gaze swept the room. "He's over there by the old piano, isn't he?"

Heather felt a tingle of excitement. If this renown expert could see him, surely the Sheffields would believe *her*. "Yes, he is. Do you see him now?"

Kathryn was staring at the exact spot where Ethan was standing. "Not clearly," she said hesitantly, "but I do see an apparition of some sort. It's very hazy, like fog, with just a faint outline. Ask him if he'll speak to me."

Heather did, but Ethan just shook his head.

She relayed the message, then added, "He hasn't spoken to me since we came in here, either. Just shakes or nods his head."

"That's probably because I'd hear him if he did. In these cases, sounds seems to be more easily transmitted than images. He's apparently determined to make this as difficult for me as possible, but there's no doubt about his presence."

She turned to Daphne. "You definitely have a spirit, Mrs. Sheffield, but it's nothing to worry about. He's a gentle, happy ghost."

Daphne paled and shuddered. "Are you absolutely certain? I don't see or feel a thing."

Jocelyn, who was sitting on the sofa next to Franchot, snuggled against him and buried her face in his shoulder. "My baby," she lamented. "I can't have Yvette exposed to a ghost. We'll have to close off this floor. I'm not taking any chances if there's even the faintest possibility that she's right."

Franchot tried to soothe his wife as Max stood quietly by the window looking thoughtful, but it was Ethan who captured Heather's attention. He hadn't moved, but his shoulders had slumped and he looked unutterably sad.

She realized that if they closed off the fourth floor he'd be all alone again. He'd no longer be able to play with his baby great-granddaughter, and it was all Heather's fault. If she hadn't blundered into his realm he'd still be a happy participant, albeit an unknown one, in the life of the family.

She should have taken the first plane back to Atlanta as soon as the Beauforts had decided she wasn't qualified for the job!

"There's nothing for you to be afraid of," Kathryn tried to assure Jocelyn. "Contrary to all the ghoulish stories you hear, spirits are seldom malevolent. This one definitely isn't."

She turned to Heather. "Now I'd like to hear your story," she said as she finally sat down. "Tell me about Ethan Hadleigh."

Once more Heather told of her encounter with the manifestation of the Sheffield family's ancestor. Kathryn listened, obviously fascinated, and interrupted every so often to ask a question or clarify a point. When it was over she sat back and sighed.

"I'm so glad you people got in touch with me," she said. "I wouldn't have missed this for anything. How could anyone possibly be frightened by this delightful apparition?"

She looked at the spot where Ethan stood. "Aren't you going to talk to me at all?" she asked him.

Heather saw him blow Kathryn a kiss, but he said nothing.

"He's grateful for your kind words," she told Kathryn. "He even blew you a kiss but he won't say anything."

Kathryn blew a kiss back at him and stood to leave.

"It's been grand meeting you, Ethan Hadleigh," she said. "I hope someday you'll trust me enough to let me see and hear you, too."

Ethan smiled and saluted, but Daphne, Lawrence and the Beauforts looked uncomfortable, as well as skeptical. Max's expression was inscrutable. Whatever he was thinking he was keeping to himself.

Back downstairs Kathryn pleaded another engagement and left after asking Heather to keep in touch with her. While they were all still saying goodbye, Max was called to the telephone.

When he returned he looked harried and spoke to Lawrence. "That was Schneider in L.A. Seems he's just learned of new evidence in the Fields custody trial that could blow his case all to hell. Dammit, I knew I should have handled that one myself. Now I've got to be out there by eight o'clock in the morning and try to piece it back together again. That means you'll have to take over the Layton hearing for me. Come to my house with me while I pick up some clothes, and I'll brief you on the way to the airport."

Lawrence nodded, and Max turned to his mother. "Sorry I have to run off, Mom. Do me a favor and put a hold on this ghost business until I get back."

He kissed her on the cheek, then walked over to Heather, who had a sinking feeling that she was being abandoned. He reached for her hand and clasped it. "Come home with me, honey," he said softly. "You can stay there tonight and come back here before Jocelyn has to go to the office in the morning."

It was all happening so fast that she couldn't think, let alone speak. Instead she just nodded and went with him.

At the house, Opal packed Max's bag while he made several phone calls, and then it was time for him to leave. Heather had simply stood by while the other three rushed around like characters in a speeded-up movie. She and Max had hardly spoken to each other, and not a word had been said about the unnerving experience with the parapsychologist.

Lawrence carried the suitcase out to the car while Max lingered at the door with Heather.

This time he put his arms around her and held her. "I'm sorry I have to leave you at a time like this," he said as he rubbed his cheek in her hair. "I wouldn't if it weren't that a friend of mine might lose custody of her two small children. Will you be all right?"

No, she wouldn't be all right. She needed him with her desperately, but she couldn't tell him that. His client needed him, too, and after all, he did have a law practice to maintain. She couldn't expect him to put her *pro bono* case above his paying ones.

"Sure, I'll be okay," she assured him. "I'm a survivor. You needn't worry about me."

Some of her disappointment must have sounded in her tone because he pulled away and looked at her. "Heather? Are you upset because I'm leaving?"

His gaze roamed over her face, seeking out her hidden uncertainties. With an effort she managed to smile. "Of course not, Max. Now run along or you'll miss your flight."

He continued to watch her. "I'm not catching a flight, I'm taking the Lear jet."

A private plane. She should have known. The Sheffields wouldn't fly commercial like everyone else.

"Well, you'd still better hurry," she said. "I'll be just fine, really."

Again he held her close and caressed her back with his gentle hands. "Then why do I get the feeling that I'm making a terrible mistake?" he murmured. "Promise you won't make any decisions until I get back?"

Any decisions made would be the Beauforts', not hers, but she didn't want to start an argument by pointing that out. "Max, I'm not crazy. You have Dr. Unger's expert opinion on that, so stop treating me as if I were incompetent."

Max's hold on her loosened, and his expression was a mask of frustration. "Goddammit," he growled, "it's me that's going crazy. Trying to deal with you is driving me right out of my mind."

He released her and walked out the door, then stopped, turned around and strode back. With a strangled groan, he took her in his arms and kissed her, hard and passionate, but before she could overcome her surprise and respond, he raised his head and muttered, "Try not to get into any more trouble while I'm away," and then he was gone.

The next morning Heather was awake before her alarm went off at six o'clock. She'd been too upset and restless to sleep well, and welcomed the necessity of getting out of bed and taking a warm, soothing shower. Afterward she pulled on the jeans she'd worn the morning before, and then let Opal persuade her to have breakfast before she walked back to the Sheffield-Beaufort home.

Max had had it written into her contract that her

days off began at 6:00 p.m. on Fridays and ended at 8:00 a.m. on Mondays, and it was six minutes to eight when she rang the doorbell. She was admitted by Inga, who told her the Beauforts and Mrs. Sheffield were having breakfast in the dining room and would like her to join them.

Although Inga made it sound like an invitation, Heather knew it was a summons that must be obeyed. Her stomach lurched, and she wished she'd skipped breakfast. That was it! Her whole future would be decided in the next hour, and Max was no longer here to protect her. She had to face them alone.

Was that why he'd jumped at the excuse to leave town so abruptly? Had he been unwilling to stand up to his mother and sister in this matter, after all?

Not that she could blame him. She was nothing but an invigorating challenge to him, but he had to live in the bosom of his family and uphold its reputation for intelligence and levelheaded good sense. An impossible task if the lady in his life was a witch. In colonial Massachusetts she'd have been burned at the stake!

A shiver ran through her at that revolting thought, and she walked into the dining room to be greeted by Daphne, Jocelyn and Franchot. Since there was no sign of the baby playing in her swing, Heather assumed that Velma was caring for her upstairs.

For some reason that fact filled her with foreboding as she accepted Franchot's invitation and sat down at the table.

After a few minutes of uneasy small talk Daphne got to the point. "Heather, we have to discuss this ghost of yours," she said cautiously, but her very choice of words increased Heather's apprehension.

"Ethan's not my ghost," she said. "He's yours."

Daphne looked a little disconcerted. "Yes, well, unfortunately we have nothing but your word that he exists. Don't you find it odd that he would appear to you, a stranger, when none of the family he supposedly represents has ever seen him?"

Heather sighed. "I don't know. I told you, I'm not a psychic. I know nothing about apparitions and have never had any interest in finding out about them. Ethan says it has something to do with losing my father so unexpectedly."

Daphne nodded. "Exactly. I suspect that subconsciously you know that this…this phantom is your mind's way of dealing with unbearable grief."

Heather tried to interrupt her, but Daphne continued. "Believe me, I know what that can do to a person. I lost a six-month-old daughter to what is now called SIDS, or crib death. It was shattering. There were times when I wasn't even sane."

There was a haunted expression on her nearly unlined face, and her usually clear hazel eyes were clouded with anguish. Suddenly she looked every one of her seventy-plus years.

Heather reacted instinctively as she reached out and put her hand over the older woman's. "Oh, Mrs. Sheffield, I'm so sorry," she murmured.

For a moment Daphne clutched Heather's hand, then with an effort she straightened and dropped her hands in her lap as she brought her emotions under control.

"Thank you," she said unsteadily, then compressed her lips for a moment before continuing. "It happened a long time ago, but I can understand how you would find solace in a ghostly manifestation. You couldn't bear the thought that your father was lost to you forever, so your mind, or psyche, if you prefer, gave you a father substitute in Ethan Hadleigh."

Heather could accept the other woman's supposition of why she saw Ethan, but not that he was a figment of her imagination. She knew better, but how could she convince Max's mother?

"But what about Dr. Unger?" Heather asked. "She agreed that there's a presence in the fourth-floor parlor. Surely you don't think she's lying."

Daphne shook her head. "No, of course not, but she admitted that she couldn't see or hear him. She really couldn't offer any proof that he was there, only a nebulous feeling."

Heather knew then what was coming, and she wasn't surprised when Franchot spoke up. "What Daphne is trying to tell you, Heather, is that we feel that you are going through a period of intense grief that has temporarily interfered with your objectivity."

Heather could see his distress as he took a deep breath and continued. "For this reason, we don't feel that you are emotionally capable of caring for a child as young as Yvette at this time. However, in going over your records I see that you were a straight-A student in mathematics, and you're familiar with computers. I know of an opening with one of the largest brokerage houses in New York City. Both the pay and the benefits are excellent, and it's yours if you want it."

Her head swam as she looked around the table at

the varying expressions of the people sitting there, distress, anxiety, even regret. It had all come to her so fast that she couldn't make sense out of it. They didn't want her working for them, but they were willing to get her a job somewhere else. At least they were being thoughtful.

Darn it, though, she wasn't hallucinating, and if she agreed to this it would be an admission that she was unbalanced. "I...I have a contract with you," she reminded him.

Franchot looked pained. "Yes, I know," he said gently, "but we'd have no trouble proving you unfit to work with children. We don't want to do that, Heather. The publicity would be unsavory for both sides, but it would hurt you far more. You'd never again be able to work as a nanny, or even a babysitter. We'll only do that if you force us to."

His threat was like a knife to her heart, but she had one more ace and she intended to use it. "I'd rather wait until Max returns before I give you an answer. After all, he is my attorney and I have a right to consult him."

Franchot looked at Daphne, and she nodded and stood. "I'd like to talk to you alone, Heather," she said in that regal tone that brooked no disobedience. "Please come up to my private quarters on the second floor."

Upstairs Heather followed Daphne into her Victorian sitting room with its high-backed sofas, floral drapes and occasional tables covered with exquisite china and porcelain figurines. They each took one of a pair of upholstered rocking chairs on either side of a small round table that held an original stained-glass Tiffany lamp.

When they'd settled themselves, Daphne spoke. "I'm going to request a very large favor of you, my dear." Her tone was kind but firm. "I have no right to ask it, and you aren't going to like it one bit, but I'm a plain-spoken woman and I see no sense in beating around the bush."

Heather shivered with apprehension and fought a compulsion to clasp her hands over her ears so she wouldn't hear what Max's mother wanted of her. Instead she twisted them together in her lap and waited.

"We in the family are well aware of Maxwell's infatuation with you," she began. "It comes as no surprise. You're a beautiful and desirable young woman. Plus you're young and naive enough to appeal to his protective instincts. He's been championing your cause ever since you first came and getting a real charge out of standing up to the rest of us."

Heather had nothing to say at this point and merely nodded as Daphne continued. "Maxwell was our baby, and I'm afraid we spoiled him rather badly. He grew up having things pretty much his own way, but after he completed his schooling and took his place in the family law firm, he refused to grow up and accept responsibility. He still wants everything to go his way no matter what the consequences."

"Mrs. Sheffield," Heather interrupted. "Could you just get to the point?" She knew she wasn't being very polite, but she couldn't stand the suspense.

"Yes, of course," Daphne said crisply. "The point is that if you're still here when Maxwell comes home, he'll take up your cause with a vengeance and to hell with the devastation his unwise enthusiasm for 'justice' will cause. Surely you can imagine the effect it would have on his future political career if the newspapers picked up the rumor that the Sheffields have a ghost, not only in their closet, but roaming all over the house and holding conversations with Maxwell's client, who is also a household employee and his current girlfriend.''

Her voice shook with conviction. "He'd be held up to ridicule in some quarters and charges of heresy in others, to say nothing of the heads of state both here and abroad who would seriously question his qualifications for a political appointment. That could also put his brothers' careers in jeopardy.''

Heather stared at the older woman disbelievingly. "Are you saying that because I see and talk to a ghost I could destroy the whole Sheffield family's power and influence? Oh, come on now, Mrs.—''

"It's possible," Daphne interrupted. "No, more than that, it's very probable. Not by yourself, of course, but if Maxwell goes on record as believing in this psychic vision of yours and defending it...well, at the very least it would ruin him. The voters don't react well to something this bizarre. I've seen brilliant careers destroyed on less.''

She leaned back and closed her eyes wearily. "If you care for him at all, you won't let him take that chance.''

Heather knew she was beaten. She'd do anything to protect Max, and that's what his mother had counted on. She was clever, but she was also speaking the truth. Publicity of that sort could be ruinous. She'd have to accept the dismissal and be grateful that they'd found her another position.

She stood slowly, feeling weighted down with her new grief. "I love Max," she said simply. "I'd never do anything to harm him, but you know that. I'll leave without a fuss and accept the job in New York, but I want to be the one to tell him. Can you give me a phone number where he can be reached."

Daphne's eyes flew open and she sat up. "No. He'd just come back here and stop you. This has to be a clean break already accomplished before he finds out about it. We can arrange to have you flown to New York this afternoon. Naturally we'll pay all your expenses until you find an apartment and get settled. You'll also get a generous severance check, but I want your promise that you won't contact Maxwell."

She, too, stood slowly, but it was the burden of years that slowed her movements. "I'll be honest with you," she said. "I don't intend to tell him where you are. He'd go after you, but I hope you'll be equally honest and admit that there's no future for the two of you together. Your backgrounds are too dissimilar. Any relationship between you would be a disaster."

Chapter Ten

Heather's defenses were shattered. There was nothing she could do but leave as gracefully as possible.

"I'll go upstairs and pack," she said. "I'd also like to say goodbye to Yvette. Surely you won't deny me that?"

A shadow of compassion flitted across Daphne's face. "No, of course I won't. I know how fond you are of the baby."

Heather turned and walked away.

On the fourth floor she again felt the welcoming warmth and headed immediately for the parlor. She had to talk to Ethan, and sounds coming from the bathroom told her that Velma would be busy in there for a while bathing the baby so she wouldn't have to worry about being disturbed.

She didn't see him when she first entered the room, but when she looked more carefully she found him standing in front of the window. Immediately she knew there was something wrong, but it took a moment to realize what it was.

He wasn't blocking her view. She could see the lace curtains right through him!

A stab of fear left her breathless. "Ethan! Are you all right? What's happening?"

"Be not afraid, my daughter," he said solemnly. "I've not changed, but you no longer have the need to see me so clearly. 'Tis a natural transition."

"That's not true," she cried, appalled at this turn of events. "I need you more than ever now."

"But don't you see," he explained. "That's why you must draw on your own inner strength. You've reached a juncture in your life when 'tis time for you to move on and put your growing-up years behind you."

"But I have..."

"Nay, not yet. You've been wrapped in the cocoon of paternal protection—"

"No! Not anymore. Daddy's been dead for over a year." Why was he saying these things? She couldn't stand it if he abandoned her, too.

"Aye, he has," Ethan agreed, "but you've still been nurtured. First in the confines of your school, then when you could no longer stay there, you found me."

"No," she protested, frantic at the thought of losing him, and pushing away the nagging suspicion that he was right. "You can't leave me. I've already lost Max. You're all I have."

A sob was ripped from her throat, and she felt tears trickling down her cheeks as she sank into the nearest chair.

"Ah, my dear child." His tone was soothing with no hint of impatience. "You can no longer rely on others for your happiness. You have strength, determination, compassion and a fine mind. All you need to face life and make of it what you will, but you must learn to use them."

The precarious restraint Heather had been keeping on her emotions splintered, and deep sobs shook her as tears streamed from her burning eyes. Ethan moved to stand beside her, but now she could see little more than an outline of him.

When her storm of weeping had passed, he spoke again. "You won't understand it now but Madam Sheffield has helped you to take your first step toward independence, and that is good."

"How can you stay that?" she exclaimed. "I love Max, and I believe he'd have learned to love me. We could have been happy together if she'd just given us a chance. I'd have given him the children we both want, and I could have learned to be a good politician's wife."

"Then why are you letting her send you away?" he asked reasonably.

She shook her head in despair. "Because at this stage of our relationship Max's mother is right. Max doesn't love me yet, but he'd defend me against his family just because I'm being unfairly dismissed. He's fiercely protective and will always fight for the underdog. That will probably turn out to be his strength, but not if he defends a sorceress this early in his career."

"Aren't you taking yourself a bit too seriously?" Ethan asked, and she could still see enough of his features to know he was smiling. "Truly, child, sorcery went out of fashion at least a hundred years ago. I'm afraid you'll have to be content with calling yourself a psychic, and they are much in favor now."

"Oh, you know what I mean," she said crossly. "I can't stay here and take the chance of damaging Max's career. If he loves me, wants me, it has to be his decision, not one forced upon him by default. I'll honor my promise to Mrs. Sheffield. I'm sure that if Max really wants to, he'll find me, but I'm not counting on that happening."

A wave of sorrow overtook her again. "I'll show you that I can take charge of my own future."

"That's my girl," he said, his tone gentle and loving. "You will make the right choices, I'm sure of it."

She truly was losing him. "W-won't I ever s-see you again?" she stammered.

"Never is a long time," he murmured, "and we have a strong bond between us. Hold me in your heart, and I will always be there for you when you really need me."

"Some people claim to have a guardian angel," she said in a hoarse whisper. "Can't you at least be mine?"

Ethan laughed, and it was a happy sound. "No one has ever accused me of being an angel before," he said teasingly, then sobered. "But I will watch over you. I cannot interfere in your decisions. You'll have to make your own mistakes, but if you believe in me I can lend you strength."

"I need your support now," she moaned, and felt tears welling once more.

"Nay, you do not need me to lean on anymore. Just have faith in yourself, and in Maxwell, and you'll live a long and happy life, I promise you."

"But—"

Her words were cut off when she saw Ethan put his finger to her lips and felt the tiny shock of electrical energy. "I'm going to leave you now, but be not sad and do not look back at what is past. Always look ahead to the future and remember me with joy, not pain."

He smiled, a heartbreakingly sweet smile, and then he was gone.

It was early afternoon when Max stepped out of the Lear jet at Boston's Logan International Airport and hurried toward the waiting limousine. For ten interminable days he'd been looking forward to getting home, and he wasn't going to waste any more time.

"Take me to Mother's house," he told Nick as he climbed into the back seat.

He'd been trying to get hold of Heather by phone for days and always just missed her. Opal said she hadn't seen her since Heather left to go back to the family home on the morning after he'd left town, and each time he called there his mother or Jocelyn insisted she was out with the baby, or gone shopping, or couldn't come to the phone for one reason or another.

At first it had been merely frustrating, then maddening, and finally frightening. Had something happened to her that nobody was telling him about? But that was unlikely. When he'd asked about her, they'd told him she was just fine.

So why in hell couldn't he get her on the telephone?

The image of her in the prim and proper skirts and blouses she wore while caring for Yvette flashed in his mind. He thought of them as her Mary Poppins outfits, but had never had the heart to tell her that they accentuated rather than disguised the soft curves of her full breasts, tiny waist and rounded hips. Nothing could have tamed the magnetic sensuality that radiated from her warm smile, her husky voice and that rolling rhythmic walk that made him itch to pull her against him.

Lord but he'd missed her! He'd given up telling himself she was just another pretty girl whom he enjoyed being with and accepted the fact that she was never going to be out of his thoughts. She'd interfered with his research, his court appearances and, most of all, with his ability to sleep.

His feelings for her were getting out of control. Imagine him, Max Sheffield, who never took anything or anybody seriously, letting a twenty-one-year-old girl tie him in emotional knots!

At the house, Max rang the doorbell and was admitted by Velma. There was no one else around as he bounded up the stairs to the fourth floor, and Heather.

But Heather wasn't there, and neither was the baby. The rooms were all neat but unoccupied, and all the furniture had been removed from the nursery!

He felt a stab of impatience. Jocelyn must have meant what she said about not using this floor as a nursery suite anymore because of the ghost. Well, he supposed he could understand that, but where had she moved it to? There weren't enough rooms on the third floor for the Beauforts' private living quarters plus a nursery and a bedroom for Heather.

The impatience of a moment ago turned to apprehension. What in hell was going on here? Where was everybody?

He turned and headed back down the stairs where he found his mother waiting for him in the hallway of the second floor. "Maxwell," she said, and there was exasperation in her tone. "Must you tear through the house like an unruly teenager?"

He stared at Daphne and his apprehension turned to dread. "Where's Heather?" There was a coldness in his tone that he'd never used with her before.

She blanched, and he knew that something was awfully wrong, but all she said was "We have to talk. Come into the sitting room."

She started to walk away, but he caught her by the shoulders and turned her around. *"Where is Heather!"* Each word was accentuated.

He saw a flash of fear in her eyes, and deeply regretted being the cause of it, but he had to have an answer.

"Heather's gone," she said, then twisted away from him and headed for the parlor.

Max was right on her heels. "Gone where?" he demanded.

"Sit down and stop being melodramatic, and I'll tell you about it." She motioned toward the high-backed sofa.

"Don't use that condescending tone with me." His escalating anger was barely controlled. "I want to know where she is, and I want to know right now."

It was Daphne who sat down. "We had to let Heather go," she said tersely.

Max hoped to God he'd heard wrong. "You *what*?" he roared.

"We had to let her go," Daphne repeated. "For heaven's sake, Maxwell, surely even you can understand that we couldn't have a nanny take care of Yvette who sees and talks to ghosts."

The violence of the emotions churning inside of him frightened Max. Heather was gone! She'd been fired and sent away. He felt as if he'd been dealt a crippling blow that finally penetrated even his thick skull and forced him to acknowledge that she was his love, his happiness, his hope for a bright future.

Without her, life wouldn't be worth living.

"Where is she?" he asked between clenched jaws.

Daphne's back straightened and she looked squarely at him. "You don't have to worry about her. Franchot found her a good position, and we're paying all her expenses until she gets resettled. She was also given a very generous severance check, so you see, everything has worked out for the best."

Max wondered if his mother was really that obtuse, or if she was just clever. He suspected the latter.

"I said *where* is she, not how is she, and I warn you to stop playing games with me."

Daphne's gaze wavered for a moment, but then held steady. "I'm not going to tell you," she said firmly. "At least not until you calm down and start thinking rationally. Believe me, son, this girl was just a diversion. You're only upset because I sent her away before your infatuation had run it's course. You'll thank me later."

Max's stomach roiled, and for a moment he was afraid he was going to be sick.

Taking a deep breath, he prayed that he could remain calm for just a few minutes longer. "Mother, I'm going to give you one more chance to tell me where Heather is. If you don't, I'm going to put a full-page ad in every major newspaper in the country offering a reward for information of her whereabouts. The media all over the world will pick it up and within minutes after the papers hit the stands I'll have her address and phone number."

He paused, then delivered his punch line. "It will also keep the gossip and rumors flying for years to come."

The blood drained from Daphne's face, and she jumped to her feet. "You wouldn't!"

"No?" he said, and picked up the phone. He dialed, then flipped the switch on the amplifier so she could hear both sides of the conversation.

"*Boston Globe*," said the voice at the other end of the line.

"This is Maxwell Sheffield. Please connect me with the editor."

"No!" Daphne cried, and hurried across the room to break the connection.

"All right," she said, and there was both resignation and defeat in her tone. "I'll tell you what you want to know."

Heather gasped as she stepped out of the air-conditioned office building where she'd been working all day and into the sweltering heat of Manhattan's financial district. Summers in Georgia had been hot, but there'd been trees and an occasional breeze to make it bearable. New York City was all concrete that held and radiated the heat, and skyscrapers that cut off any chance of a cooling current of air.

The sidewalk burned through the leather soles of her pumps as she hurried toward her temporary home. Thank goodness it was only a few blocks from where she worked. She was afraid of the subway, and no working girl could afford twice-a-day taxi service.

Skirting street vendors, scattered trash and an occasional street person pushing a shopping cart, she speeded up her pace. Her heart went out to the homeless men and women with whom she came in contact during her morning and afternoon treks. It was bad enough for them in the summer, but how could they possibly survive the freezing winters?

Heather's footsteps slowed as she caught sight of the genteelly shabby hotel where the Sheffields had arranged for her to stay until she could find an apartment. A nearly impossible task in Manhattan, but she was determined to overcome the odds as quickly as possible.

She didn't want to be dependent on them any longer than necessary. Not that she was accepting their charity. The Sheffields owed her, and they knew it. She had a valid contract and could probably have won if she'd filed a lawsuit against them.

Quickly she shut down that line of thinking. Bitterness would bring her nothing but unhappiness, and they'd been fair in most of their dealings with her. If only they had let her say goodbye to Max before she left.

She missed him so much! She'd been in such a

state of shock and confusion while making her hurried exit from Boston that she hadn't fully understood the extent of all she was giving up, until she'd spent her first night alone in an impersonal hotel in a strange and frightening city.

In just a few agonizing hours she'd lost Max, Ethan, the baby she'd become so attached to and the home and position that represented security to her. For the second time in a year her life had fallen apart, and she was still reeling from the blow.

Walking through the glass doors of the hotel, she stopped at the desk to get her room key. The bell captain had warned her that it was better to leave it there when she went out than to take a chance of its being stolen from her in this crime-ridden metropolis.

Exiting the slow-moving elevator on the seventh floor, she walked down the rose carpeting of the hall and let herself into her room. It was a nice place, large and comfortably furnished, with a wide picture window that looked out onto the side of another elderly brick building but provided plenty of light.

Kicking off her shoes she headed for the bathroom and a cool shower. She'd quickly learned that by having a hot lunch at the cafeteria in her office building and keeping munchies in her room to snack on at night, she could save a lot of money over eating dinner in the hotel dining room. Also she hated to eat alone in a restaurant, and she'd been invited to share a table at lunch with several of the friendly people she worked with.

The cool, pulsating spray of water relaxed her, but also left her vulnerable to the loneliness that she managed to shut out during her hours at work. Evenings were when thoughts of Max tormented her. She had only to close her eyes to see him smiling at her, his eyes shimmering with affection.

He *had* felt something for her, she couldn't be wrong about that. He'd told her, not with words, but with the tenderness of his touch and the protective way he treated her, as though she were precious to him.

She shook her head to clear it and turned off the shower. Fantasizing about Maxwell Sheffield brought her nothing but anguish, and she was determined to stop it. It had been ten days since she'd left Boston. With all his resources, that was plenty of time for him to find her if he'd wanted to.

His mother had been right. She'd caught his attention, aroused his libido and responded with flattering eagerness to his tentative lovemaking, but he'd started to pull away even before he left for Los Angeles. The night she'd spent with him at his house, he'd hardly spoken to her, let alone made a pass.

She pulled on her red shorts and red-and-white striped cotton knit shirt but shunned shoes. After wearing high-heeled pumps all day, she liked to pad around barefoot at home.

She was standing in front of the mirror blow-drying her hair and listening to the news on television when there was a knock at her door. Startled, she shut off the blow-drier and put it down.

Who could that be? She hadn't ordered anything from room service, and the people at work had warned her repeatedly never to open her door unless she knew who was on the other side.

Switching off the television, she walked closer and called. "Who is it?"

There was a slight pause, then, "It's Max, Heather."

Her whole nervous system responded to the sound of his voice, and her heart pounded as she moved closer and looked through the peephole. It was Max, all right, but he looked different. His hair was mussed, and although he wore a suit, it was rumpled; his tie was missing and his shirt was unbuttoned at the throat.

Her first inclination was to open the door and throw herself into his arms, but she quickly stifled it. She'd promised Ethan that she'd start acting like a responsible adult, and that's what she intended to do.

"What do you want?" she asked with as much reserve as she could muster.

He winced, as though her coolness pained him. "I want to see you, talk to you. Please let me in." There was an unmistakable note of pleading in his tone.

She couldn't bear to make him stand out there in the hall answering questions.

Pushing back the two bolts, she opened the locked door and stood aside to let him enter.

His gaze roamed over her as she shut the door behind him, and she was shocked to see that he looked not only disheveled but actually ill. His face was pale and lined with weariness, and his usual buoyancy had been replaced with a discouraged slump.

She swallowed back a groan of dismay. "How did you find me?"

"Did you really think I wouldn't," he asked sadly.

She blinked. "Well...it's been ten days. I figured

you weren't interested enough to go to all the trouble.''

Max's arms ached to hold her, but he could tell by her tone and her expression that he'd better not try it. He was terrified of making her so angry that she'd send him away without listening to him. He reached out and fingered a strand of the raven hair that bounced around her shoulders. It felt clean and soft and vibrant, just as he knew she would if he dared touch her.

"I really have been a selfish bastard, haven't I?'' His voice wasn't altogether steady. "I've basked in your generous affection and given you nothing in return.''

As he wound his finger in her hair, the slight tug on her scalp sent tingles all the way down her spine. "Don't say that,'' she protested. "You've been wonderful to me. You took me sight-seeing, talked the Beauforts into hiring me, negotiated my contract and—''

"And walked off and left you at the mercy of my autocratic family when you needed me the most,'' he said, his tone heavy with self-disgust.

So that was it. He'd come home and found her gone, and now his conscience was bothering him because his sister had fired her while he was away.

It took all of her determination to step backward, and with a gentle movement of her head disengaged his finger from her hair. "That wasn't your fault, Max,'' she said and clenched her hands together to keep from giving in to the compelling desire to stroke the lines of anxiety that creased his forehead. "You had urgent business in California that needed to be dealt with immediately. I understand.''

He shook his head slowly. ''No, sweetheart, I don't think you do, because I didn't understand it myself until today. There's nothing more important to me than you. Absolutely nothing, but I was too self-centered and just plain scared to admit it until I came home this afternoon and found you gone.''

Heather stared at him, too dumbfounded to react. What was he saying? Did he mean he had strong feelings for her, or just that he'd been acting as her attorney at the time and shouldn't have left before the business with the ghost was resolved?

She swallowed and found her voice. ''I...I don't know what you mean.''

Max was sweating even though the room was air-conditioned. If he messed up and she sent him away, he wasn't sure he could stand it. If only he could crush her in his arms and kiss her until nothing else mattered but the two of them, together, but it was much too late for such a simple solution.

It was no longer enough to just tell her how he felt, he also had to convince her, and he wasn't sure she'd ever believe him after the shameful way he and his family had treated her.

He was beginning to feel light-headed. He hadn't been sleeping well all week, and that morning he'd been so anxious to get back to Heather that he'd insisted they take off at daylight. He'd rolled out of bed at 4:00 a.m. in order to get to the busy, sprawling airport in time, and they'd flown from L.A. to Boston, with only a quick stop in Denver to refuel. Then, after the shocking events in Boston, they'd been airborne again for the flight to Kennedy Airport in New York.

Apparently it was all starting to catch up with him.

A glance around the room told him that there was only one chair plus the bed to sit on. "Do you mind if we sit down," he asked.

"No, of course not, please do," Heather said, and realized that her first impression had been right. He was either ill or exhausted.

She motioned to the chair, but he lowered himself to the edge of the bed. "This will be fine," he said. "You take the chair."

She didn't immediately move but stood watching him. "Max, you don't look well. Can I get you something?"

He smiled, and seemed grateful for her concern. "Does this hotel have room service? I haven't eaten since lunch yesterday."

Without waiting to comment, she went to the phone and ordered soup and club sandwiches for two, then walked back to the bed and sat down beside him. "Okay," she said, her tone brusque with anxiety, "Tell me what's upset you so."

He reached over and took her hand. It was soft and warm, and he clung to it and breathed a sigh of relief when she didn't draw away. "You really don't know, do you?" he said with astonishment.

Her smoky-blue eyes widened, and she shook her head. "No, I don't. Did you say you just got back from Los Angeles today?"

"Yes. I didn't know until a few hours ago that you'd been sent away. I'm still suffering from shock and rage. Every time I asked to talk to you on the phone, I was told that you were either out or busy. I had no idea that you weren't still there.''

Heather was confused. ''But how did you find out that I was here, in New York, at this address? Your mother—''

''My mother has finally learned not to treat me like an idiot child,'' Max said grimly. ''I think I can safely say that she'll never again interfere in my personal life.''

Heather should have been overjoyed, but the nagging doubt Mrs. Sheffield had planted in her mind was still there. Was making his mother tell him where she was just a point of pride with him, or did he really want her?

As though reading her mind, he moved closer and cupped her head in his hands, tilting her face upward to meet his gaze. ''I love you,'' he said simply, and made her heart leap. ''I've fought it, refused to recognize it and finally run away from it, but the full force of that love hit me with a stunning blow when I learned that you were gone and I'd probably lost you.''

He touched his lips to hers and stroked his fingers through her hair. ''Between Mother and me, we've probably dampened any feelings you may have had for me, but I'm asking you...no, I'm begging you...to give me another chance. Come back to Boston with me, and let me court you. I promise to do it right this time.''

He pressed tiny kisses to her closed eyelids, and she felt her resolve melting in the heat of the need he was building in her.

In the back of her mind she knew this wasn't right,

she had to stop him, but when she put her hands on his chest to push him away she felt the flesh and muscles beneath his shirt.

His heart was pounding as fiercely as her own and a little moan of distress escaped her. "Oh, Max, please..." She wasn't sure whether she meant "please don't," or "please do."

He put his arms around her and drew her close, and she knew she had to act or she'd be lost.

With a gentle shove she pushed him away. "No, Max," she said sadly, "don't do this to me. A relationship between us has no future, and much as I love you, I can't live that way. When we eventually broke up it would destroy me."

He looked at her and frowned. "You don't honestly think I'd let you go once I had you, do you? I want to marry you, sweetheart, not just have a relationship."

That brought her to her senses fast. "Marry me!" She stood. "That's not even an option. The Sheffield men don't marry the household help, especially the ones who see ghosts. Your hopes for a political career would go right down the drain."

Max blanched and got to his feet. Grabbing her by the shoulders, he turned her to face him. "Stop that, Heather," he ordered. "You know something? You're a reverse snob. Where did you ever get the idea that..."

His voice trailed off and a look of dawning comprehension replaced the outrage in his expression. When he spoke again his voice was filled with regret. "My mother really did a number on you, didn't she?"

He gathered her back into his embrace. "Tell me what she said to you."

Heather knew that if there was any hope of a future for her with Max, there could be no half-truths or evasions between them now. "She said you'd never marry me. That I wasn't qualified to be the wife of a politician. That if word got out that I claimed to see a ghost in the Sheffield home, one who conversed with me, it would ruin your hopes for political office, and may even damage your brothers' careers."

She buried her face in his shoulder. "I had no choice but to agree to leave and not contact you ever again."

His arms tightened around her, and he nuzzled her throat. "Mother was way off base, but even if she hadn't been, there's something you don't know, sweetheart," he murmured. "I've never told anyone, but now I realize it was wrong not to have spoken up years ago. I've never wanted a career in politics. I don't even want to be a partner in the family law firm."

Heather couldn't believe what she'd heard and raised her head to look at him. "But of course you do," she protested. "Your mother said..."

"That's right," he interrupted. "My mother said it was my duty to follow the family tradition, and I never questioned it. My dad and brothers chose legal careers as a springboard to go on to high government positions, and the power that goes with them. I studied to be an attorney so that I could practice law, not politics."

"But you have a law practice..."

He shook his head. "Not really. Mostly I'm a law

clerk and errand boy in training for an important government appointment when I'm a little older and more experienced, but that's my family's wishes, not mine."

Almost as if he couldn't resist, he lowered his head and kissed her, a sweet, gentle kiss filled with caring. "Do you want to know what I'd like to do with my legal training?"

She relaxed against him and put her arms around his neck. "Very much," she whispered against his ear.

He rubbed her cheek with his own. "I'd like to open an office in the poorer section of a city in some other part of the country and help folks who need a lawyer but can't afford the big firms. I have more money than I can ever spend so I could charge only what the client can pay."

His tone had taken on a dreamy quality. "There are so many people who are neither rich nor poor and have no access to legal representation because they fall between the cracks financially. It's not right, and I'd like to help them."

He leaned back slightly so he could look at her. "I wouldn't expect you to live in that area," he assured her. "We could buy a home in the nicest part of town, and..."

"You wouldn't be very effective if you tried to straddle two worlds," she interrupted. "I'd be much more comfortable living among the people you plan to represent, that's more like my own background. I could help in the office, maybe get some paralegal training..."

She saw that he was grinning and realized what she was saying.

"Does that mean you will marry me, after all?" he asked, and she could feel the tension in him as he waited for her answer.

"Oh, darling," she murmured uncertainly, "are you sure?"

The tension went out of him, and he hugged her so tightly that she could scarcely breath. "I've never been more sure of anything in my life. I love you so much."

"I love you, too," she murmured, and lifted her head for another kiss.

This one started gently, but quickly deepened to a nipping of lips and a dueling of tongues that sent heat coursing through her body. When they came up for air, they were lying on the bed, with Max sprawled partially across her.

"I hope you're not going to insist on a long engagement," he said anxiously.

Some of her exuberance dimmed. "I guess that will depend on how your family takes the news," she answered.

Max frowned. "My family has nothing to say about it. I'd marry you tonight if I could get a license." He sighed and put his hand on her bare thigh. "How about your ghost? Is he coming to live with us?"

"How do you feel about my ghost?" she asked uneasily. "Do you still think he's just a figment of my imagination?"

Max kneaded her leg tenderly. "No, sweetheart, I know you didn't imagine him. If you say he stays in the parlor on the fourth floor I believe you. Jocelyn believes it, too, or she wouldn't have moved her household to a condominium on the other side of Boston."

Heather's eyes widened. "Did she really? I'm sorry about that. Ethan would never hurt anybody, and he took such pleasure in the baby."

She pulled Max's head down to lie between her breasts. "To answer your question, no, my ghost won't be living with us. He no longer appears to me. He said I should grow up and have faith in you, and promised that if I did I'd have a long and happy life."

Max pulled her shirt up and kissed her bare breast. "I appreciate his trust," he said seriously. "I'll spend the rest of my life trying to keep you happy."

He put his hand back on her thigh and stroked it as he took her throbbing nipple in his mouth. Prickly flames of fire trailed to the core of her womanhood, and she arched against him as his mouth again took hers in a searing union that set her ablaze.

She heard the sound of knocking several times before a male voice from outside the door called. "Miss Carmichael, room service. I have your order."

Max lifted his head and muttered something indelicate. "Tell him to go away," he growled.

Heather's heart was pounding, and her breathing came in gasps. "But you said you were hungry," she said breathlessly.

"I am," he said. "Starving, but not for food. Tell him to leave it in the hall and we'll get it later."

She'd finally managed to pull herself together enough to slide out from under Max. "You haven't eaten since yesterday,'' she reminded him. "You need the nourishment.''

He groaned. "You've got a lot to learn about men,'' he said as he sat up. "If I agree to eat can we take up where we left off later?''

She crawled off the bed and stood. "Would that make you happy?'' This time there was no teasing in her tone.

He climbed out of bed and cupped her shoulders with his hands. His gaze sought hers, and his expression was tender. "Only if it's what you want, too,'' he assured her gently.

She put out her hand and stroked his temple. "It's what I want, too,'' she whispered, and he gathered her in his arms as the banging on the door continued dimly in the background.

* * * * * *

Silhouette.

SPECIAL EDITION ™

SPECIAL EDITION

Stories of love and life, these powerful novels are tales that you can identify with— romances with "something special" added in!

Fall in love with the stories of authors such as **Nora Roberts, Diana Palmer, Ginna Gray** and many more of your special favorites—as well as wonderful new voices!

Special Edition brings you entertainment for the heart!

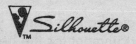

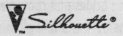

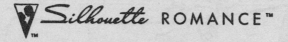

Silhouette ROMANCE™

What's a single dad to do when he needs a wife by next Thursday?

Who's a confirmed bachelor to call when he finds a baby on his doorstep?

How does a plain Jane in love with her gorgeous boss get him to notice her?

From classic love stories to romantic comedies to emotional heart tuggers, **Silhouette Romance** offers six irresistible novels every month by some of your favorite authors! Such as...beloved bestsellers **Diana Palmer, Annette Broadrick, Suzanne Carey, Elizabeth August** and **Marie Ferrarella**, to name just a few—and some sure to become favorites!

Fabulous Fathers...Bundles of Joy...Miniseries... Months of blushing brides and convenient weddings... Holiday celebrations... You'll find all this and much more in **Silhouette Romance**—always emotional, always enjoyable, always about love!

SR-GEN

SILHOUETTE®
Desire®

Do you want...

Dangerously handsome heroes

Evocative, everlasting love stories

Sizzling and tantalizing sensuality

Incredibly sexy miniseries like **MAN OF THE MONTH**

Red-hot romance

Enticing entertainment that can't be beat!

You'll find all of this, and much *more* each and every month in **SILHOUETTE DESIRE**. Don't miss these unforgettable love stories by some of romance's hottest authors. Silhouette Desire—where your fantasies will always come true....

Harlequin® Historical

From rugged lawmen and
valiant knights to defiant heiresses
and spirited frontierswomen,
Harlequin Historicals will
capture your imagination with
their dramatic scope, passion
and adventure.

Harlequin Historicals...
they're too good to miss!